MATHEMATICAL MONOGRAPHS.

EDITED BY

Mansfield Merriman and Robert S. Woodward.

Octavo, Cloth, $1.00 each.

No. 1. HISTORY OF MODERN MATHEMATICS.
By DAVID EUGENE SMITH.

No. 2. SYNTHETIC PROJECTIVE GEOMETRY.
By GEORGE BRUCE HALSTED.

No. 3. DETERMINANTS.
By LAENAS GIFFORD WELD.

No. 4. HYPERBOLIC FUNCTIONS.
By JAMES McMAHON.

No. 5. HARMONIC FUNCTIONS.
By WILLIAM E. BYERLY.

No. 6. GRASSMANN'S SPACE ANALYSIS.
By EDWARD W. HYDE.

No. 7. PROBABILITY AND THEORY OF ERRORS.
By ROBERT S. WOODWARD.

No. 8. VECTOR ANALYSIS AND QUATERNIONS.
By ALEXANDER MACFARLANE.

No. 9. DIFFERENTIAL EQUATIONS.
By WILLIAM WOOLSEY JOHNSON.

No. 10. THE SOLUTION OF EQUATIONS.
By MANSFIELD MERRIMAN.

No. 11. FUNCTIONS OF A COMPLEX VARIABLE.
By THOMAS S. FISKE.

PUBLISHED BY

JOHN WILEY & SONS, NEW YORK.

CHAPMAN & HALL, Limited, LONDON.

MATHEMATICAL MONOGRAPHS.

EDITED BY

MANSFIELD MERRIMAN AND ROBERT S. WOODWARD.

No. 5.

HARMONIC FUNCTIONS.

BY

WILLIAM E. BYERLY,

PROFESSOR OF MATHEMATICS IN HARVARD UNIVERSITY.

FOURTH EDITION, ENLARGED.

FIRST THOUSAND.

NEW YORK:

JOHN WILEY & SONS.

LONDON: CHAPMAN & HALL, LIMITED.

1906.

ROBERT DRUMMOND, PRINTER, NEW YORK.

EDITORS' PREFACE.

THE volume called Higher Mathematics, the first edition of which was published in 1896, contained eleven chapters by eleven authors, each chapter being independent of the others, but all supposing the reader to have at least a mathematical training equivalent to that given in classical and engineering colleges. The publication of that volume is now discontinued and the chapters are issued in separate form. In these reissues it will generally be found that the monographs are enlarged by additional articles or appendices which either amplify the former presentation or record recent advances. This plan of publication has been arranged in order to meet the demand of teachers and the convenience of classes, but it is also thought that it may prove advantageous to readers in special lines of mathematical literature.

It is the intention of the publishers and editors to add other monographs to the series from time to time, if the call for the same seems to warrant it. Among the topics which are under consideration are those of elliptic functions, the theory of numbers, the group theory, the calculus of variations, and non-Euclidean geometry; possibly also monographs on branches of astronomy, mechanics, and mathematical physics may be included. It is the hope of the editors that this form of publication may tend to promote mathematical study and research over a wider field than that which the former volume has occupied.

December, 1905.

iii

10406

AUTHOR'S PREFACE.

THIS brief sketch of the Harmonic Functions and their use in Mathematical Physics was written as a chapter of Merriman and Woodward's Higher Mathematics. It was intended to give enough in the way of introduction and illustration to serve as a useful part of the equipment of the general mathematical student, and at the same time to point out to one specially interested in the subject the way to carry on his study and reading toward a broad and detailed knowledge of its more difficult portions.

Fourier's Series, Zonal Harmonics, and Bessel's Functions of the order zero are treated at considerable length, with the intention of enabling the reader to use them in actual work in physical problems, and to this end several valuable numerical tables are included in the text.

CAMBRIDGE, MASS., December, 1905.

CONTENTS.

Art. 1. History and Description . . . . Page 7
      2. Homogeneous Linear Differential Equations 10
      3. Problem in Trigonometric Series 12
      4. Problem in Zonal Harmonics. 15
      5. Problem in Bessel's Functions 21
      6. The Sine Series 26
      7. The Cosine Series 30
      8. Fourier's Series 32
      9. Extension of Fourier's Series 34
     10. Dirichlet's Conditions 36
     11. Applications of Trigonometric Series 38
     12. Properties of Zonal Harmonics 40
     13. Problems in Zonal Harmonics 43
     14. Additional Forms 45
     15. Development in Terms of Zonal Harmonics 46
     16. Formulas for Development 47
     17. Formulas in Zonal Harmonics 50
     18. Spherical Harmonics 51
     19. Bessel's Functions. Properties 52
     20. Applications of Bessel's Functions 53
     21. Development in Terms of Bessel's Functions 55
     22. Problems in Bessel's Functions 58
     23. Bessel's Functions of Higher Order 59
     24. Lamé's Functions 59

Table I. Surface Zonal Harmonics 60
      II. Bessel's Functions 62
     III. Roots of Bessel's Functions 63
      IV. Values of $J_0(xi)$ 63

Index 65

HARMONIC FUNCTIONS.

ART. 1. HISTORY AND DESCRIPTION.

What is known as the Harmonic Analysis owed its origin and development to the study of concrete problems in various branches of Mathematical Physics, which however all involved the treatment of partial differential equations of the same general form.

The use of Trigonometric Series was first suggested by Daniel Bernouilli in 1753 in his researches on the musical vibrations of stretched elastic strings, although Bessel's Functions had been already (1732) employed by him and by Euler in dealing with the vibrations of a heavy string suspended from one end; and Zonal and Spherical Harmonics were introduced by Legendre and Laplace in 1782 in dealing with the attraction of solids of revolution.

The analysis was greatly advanced by Fourier in 1812–1824 in his remarkable work on the Conduction of Heat, and important additions have been made by Lamé (1839) and by a host of modern investigators.

The differential equations treated in the problems which have just been enumerated are

$$\frac{\partial^2 y}{\partial t^2} = a^2 \frac{\partial^2 y}{\partial x^2} \qquad \textbf{(1)}$$

for the transverse vibrations of a musical string;

$$\frac{\partial^2 y}{\partial t^2} = c^2\left(x\frac{\partial^2 y}{\partial x^2} + \frac{\partial y}{\partial x}\right) \tag{2}$$

for small transverse vibrations of a uniform heavy string suspended from one end;

$$\frac{\partial^2 V}{\partial x^2} + \frac{\partial^2 V}{\partial y^2} + \frac{\partial^2 V}{\partial z^2} = 0, \tag{3}$$

which is Laplace's equation; and

$$\frac{\partial u}{\partial t} = a^2\left(\frac{\partial^2 u}{\partial x^2} + \frac{\partial^2 u}{\partial y^2} + \frac{\partial^2 u}{\partial z^2}\right) \tag{4}$$

for the conduction of heat in a homogeneous solid.

Of these Laplace's equation (3), and (4) of which (3) is a special case, are by far the most important, and we shall concern ourselves mainly with them in this chapter. As to their interest to engineers and physicists we quote from an article in The Electrician of Jan. 26, 1894, by Professor John Perry:

"There is a well-known partial differential equation, which is the same in problems on heat-conduction, motion of fluids, the establishment of electrostatic or electromagnetic potential, certain motions of viscous fluid, certain kinds of strain and stress, currents in a conductor, vibrations of elastic solids, vibrations of flexible strings or elastic membranes, and innumerable other phenomena. The equation has always to be solved subject to certain boundary or limiting conditions, sometimes as to space and time, sometimes as to space alone, and we know that if we obtain any solution of a particular problem, then that is the true and only solution. Furthermore, if a solution, say, of a heat-conduction problem is obtained by any person, that answer is at once applicable to analogous problems in all the other departments of physics. Thus, if Lord Kelvin draws for us the lines of flow in a simple vortex, he has drawn for us the lines of magnetic force about a circular current: if Lord Rayleigh calculates for us the resistance of the mouth of an organ-pipe, he has also determined the end effect of a bar of iron which is magnetized; when Mr. Oliver Heaviside shows his matchless skill and familiarity with Bessel's functions in solving electromagnetic problems, he is solving problems in heat-conductivity or the strains in prismatic shafts. How difficult it is to express exactly the distribution of strain in a twisted square shaft, for example, and yet how easy it is to understand thoroughly when one knows the perfect-fluid analogy! How easy, again, it is to imagine the electric current density everywhere in a conductor when transmitting alternating currents when we know Mr. Heaviside's viscous-fluid analogy, or even the heat-conduction analogy!

" Much has been written about the correlation of the physical sciences; but when we observe how a young man who has worked almost altogether at heat problems suddenly shows himself acquainted with the most difficult investigations in other departments of physics, we may say that the true correlation of the physical sciences lies in the equation of continuity

$$\frac{\partial u}{\partial t} = a^2 \left(\frac{\partial^2 u}{\partial x^2} + \frac{\partial^2 u}{\partial y^2} + \frac{\partial^2 u}{\partial z^2} \right)."$$

In the Theory of the Potential Function in the Attraction of Gravitation, and in Electrostatics and Electrodynamics,[*] V in Laplace's equation (3) is the value of the Potential Function, at any external point (x, y, z), due to any distribution of matter or of electricity; in the theory of the Conduction of Heat in a homogeneous solid [†] V is the temperature at any point in the solid after the stationary temperatures have been established, and in the theory of the irrotational flow of an incompressible fluid [‡] V is the Velocity Potential Function and (3) is known as the equation of continuity.

If we use spherical coördinates, (3) takes the form

$$\frac{1}{r^2} \left[r \frac{\partial^2 (rV)}{\partial r^2} + \frac{1}{\sin \theta} \frac{\partial \left(\sin \theta \frac{\partial V}{\partial \theta} \right)}{\partial \theta} + \frac{1}{\sin^2 \theta} \frac{\partial^2 V}{\partial \phi^2} \right] = 0; \quad (5)$$

[*] See Peirce's Newtonian Potential Function. Boston.

[†] See Fourier's Analytic Theory of Heat. London and New York, 1878 ; or Riemann's Partielle Differentialgleichungen. Brunswick.

[‡] See Lamb's Hydrodynamics. London and New York, 1895.

and if we use cylindrical coördinates, the form

$$\frac{\partial^2 V}{\partial r^2} + \frac{1}{r}\frac{\partial V}{\partial r} + \frac{1}{r^2}\frac{\partial^2 V}{\partial \phi^2} + \frac{\partial^2 V}{\partial z^2} = 0. \tag{6}$$

In the theory of the Conduction of Heat in a homogeneous solid,* u in equation (4) is the temperature of any point (x, y, z) of the solid at any time t, and a^2 is a constant determined by experiment and depending on the conductivity and the thermal capacity of the solid.

Art. 2. Homogeneous Linear Differential Equations.

The general solution of a differential equation is the equation expressing the most general relation between the primitive variables which is consistent with the given differential equation and which does not involve differentials or derivatives. A general solution will always contain arbitrary (i.e., undetermined) constants or arbitrary functions.

A particular solution of a differential equation is a relation between the primitive variables which is consistent with the given differential equation, but which is less general than the general solution, although included in it.

Theoretically, every particular solution can be obtained from the general solution by substituting in the general solution particular values for the arbitrary constants or particular functions for the arbitrary functions; but in practice it is often easy to obtain particular solutions directly from the differential equation when it would be difficult or impossible to obtain the general solution.

(*a*) If a problem requiring for its solution the solving of a differential equation is determinate, there must always be given in addition to the differential equation enough outside conditions for the determination of all the arbitrary constants or arbitrary functions that enter into the general solution of the equation; and in dealing with such a problem, if the differential equation can be readily solved the natural method of procedure is to obtain its general solution, and then to determine the constants or functions by the aid of the given conditions.

It often happens, however, that the general solution of the differential equation in question cannot be obtained, and then, since the problem, if determinate, will be solved, if by any means a solution of the equation can be found which will also satisfy the given outside conditions, it is worth while to try to get particular solutions and so to combine them as to form a result which shall satisfy the given conditions without ceasing to satisfy the differential equation.

(*b*) A differential equation is linear when it would be of the first degree if the dependent variable and all its derivatives were regarded as algebraic unknown quantities. If it is linear and contains no term which does not involve the dependent variable or one of its derivatives, it is said to be linear and homogeneous.

All the differential equations given in Art. 1 are linear and homogeneous.

(*c*) If a value of the dependent variable has been found which satisfies a given homogeneous, linear, differential equation, the product formed by multiplying this value by any constant will also be a value of the dependent variable which will satisfy the equation.

For if all the terms of the given equation are transposed to the first member, the substitution of the first-named value must reduce that member to zero; substituting the second value is equivalent to multiplying each term of the result of the first substitution by the same constant factor, which therefore may be taken out as a factor of the whole first member. The remaining factor being zero, the product is zero and the equation is satisfied.

(*d*) If several values of the dependent variable have been found each of which satisfies the given differential equation, their sum will satisfy the equation; for if the sum of the values in question is substituted in the equation, each term of the sum will give rise to a set of terms which must be equal to zero, and therefore the sum of these sets must be zero.

(e) It is generally possible to get by some simple device particular solutions of such differential equations as those we have collected in Art. 1. The object of this chapter is to find methods of so combining these particular solutions as to satisfy any given conditions which are consistent with the nature of the problem in question.

This often requires us to be able to develop any given function of the variables which enter into the expression of these conditions in terms of normal forms suited to the problem with which we happen to be dealing, and suggested by the form of particular solution that we are able to obtain for the differential equation.

These normal forms are frequently sines and cosines, but they are often much more complicated functions known as Legendre's Coefficients, or Zonal Harmonics; Laplace's Coefficients, or Spherical Harmonics; Bessel's Functions, or Cylindrical Harmonics; Lamé's Functions, or Ellipsoidal Harmonics; etc.

ART. 3.   PROBLEM IN TRIGONOMETRIC SERIES.

As an illustration let us consider the following problem: A large iron plate π centimeters thick is heated throughout to a uniform temperature of 100 degrees centigrade; its faces are then suddenly cooled to the temperature zero and are kept at that temperature for 5 seconds. What will be the temperature of a point in the middle of the plate at the end of that time?   Given $a^2 = 0.185$ in C.G.S. units.

Take the origin of coördinates in one face of the plate and the axis of X perpendicular to that face, and let u be the temperature of any point in the plate t seconds after the cooling begins.

We shall suppose the flow of heat to be directly across the plate so that at any given time all points in any plane parallel to the faces of the plate will have the same temperature. Then u depends upon a single space-coordinate x; $\dfrac{\partial u}{\partial y} = 0$ and $\dfrac{\partial u}{\partial z} = 0$, and (4), Art. 1, reduces to

$$\frac{\partial u}{\partial t} = a^2 \frac{\partial^2 u}{\partial x^2}. \tag{1}$$

Obviously, $\qquad u = 100°$ when $t = 0$, $\qquad\qquad$ (2)

$$u = \quad 0 \text{ when } x = 0, \tag{3}$$

and $\qquad\qquad u = \quad 0 \text{ when } x = \pi;$ $\qquad\qquad$ (4)

and we need to find a solution of (1) which satisfies the conditions (2), (3), and (4).

We shall begin by getting a particular solution of (1), and we shall use a device which always succeeds when the equation is linear and homogeneous and has constant coefficients.

Assume * $u = e^{\beta x + \gamma t}$, where β and γ are constants; substitute in (1) and divide through by $e^{\beta x + \gamma t}$ and we get $\gamma = a^2 \beta^2$; and if this condition is satisfied, $u = e^{\beta x + \gamma t}$ is a solution of (1).

$u = e^{\beta x + a^2 \beta^2 t}$ is then a solution of (1) no matter what the value of β.

We can modify the form of this solution with advantage. Let $\beta = \mu i$,† then $u = e^{-a^2 \mu^2 t} e^{\mu x i}$ is a solution of (1), as is also $u = e^{-a^2 \mu^2 t} e^{-\mu x i}$.

By (d), Art. 2,

$$u = e^{-a^2 \mu^2 t} \frac{\left(e^{\mu x i} + e^{-\mu x i}\right)}{2} = e^{-a^2 \mu^2 t} \cos \mu x \tag{5}$$

is a solution, as is also

$$u = e^{-a^2 \mu^2 t} \frac{\left(e^{\mu x i} - e^{-\mu x i}\right)}{2i} = e^{-a^2 \mu^2 t} \sin \mu x; \tag{6}$$

and μ is entirely arbitrary.

---

* This assumption must be regarded as purely tentative. It must be tested by substituting in the equation, and is justified if it leads to a solution.

† The letter i will be used to represent $\sqrt{-1}$.

By giving different values to μ we get different particular solutions of (1); let us try to so combine them as to satisfy our conditions while continuing to satisfy equation (1).

$u = e^{-a^2\mu^2 t} \sin \mu x$ is zero when $x = 0$ for all values of μ; it is zero when $x = \pi$ if μ is a whole number. If, then, we write u equal to a sum of terms of the form $A e^{-a^2 m^2 t} \sin mx$, where m is an integer, we shall have a solution of (1) (see (d), Art. 2) which satisfies (3) and (4).

Let this solution be

$$u = A_1 e^{-a^2 t} \sin x + A_2 e^{-4a^2 t} \sin 2x + A_3 e^{-9a^2 t} \sin 3x + \dots, \quad (7)$$

$A_1, A_2, A_3, \dots$ being undetermined constants.

When $t = 0$, (7) reduces to

$$u = A_1 \sin x + A_2 \sin 2x + A_3 \sin 3x + \dots . \quad (8)$$

If now it is possible to develop unity into a series of the form (8) we have only to substitute the coefficients of that series each multiplied by 100 for $A_1, A_2, A_3 \dots$ in (7) to have a solution satisfying (1) and all the equations of condition (2), (3), and (4).

We shall prove later (see Art. 6) that

$$1 = \frac{4}{\pi}\left[\sin x + \frac{1}{3}\sin 3x + \frac{1}{5}\sin 5x + \dots\right]$$

for all values of x between 0 and π. Hence our solution is

$$u = \frac{400}{\pi}\left[e^{-a^2 t}\sin x + \frac{1}{3}e^{-9a^2 t}\sin 3x + \frac{1}{5}e^{-25a^2 t}\sin 5x + \dots\right] (9)$$

To get the answer of the numerical problem we have only to compute the value of u when $x = \frac{\pi}{2}$ and $t = 5$ seconds. As there is no object in going beyond tenths of a degree, four-place tables will more than suffice, and no term of (9) beyond the first will affect the result. Since $\sin \frac{\pi}{2} = 1$, we have to compute the numerical value of

$$\frac{400}{\pi}e^{-a^2t} \quad \text{where} \quad a^2 = 0.185 \quad \text{and} \quad t = 5.$$

$$\log a^2 = 9.2672 - 10 \qquad \log 400 = 2.6021$$
$$\log t = 0.6990 \qquad \operatorname{colog} \pi = 9.5059 - 10$$
$$\log a^2t = 9.9662 - 10 \qquad \operatorname{colog} e^{a^2t} = 9.5982 - 10$$
$$\log \log e = 9.6378 - 10$$
$$\log \log e^{a^2t} = 9.6040 - 10 \qquad \log u = 1.7062$$
$$\log e^{a^2t} = 0.4018 \qquad u = 50°.8.$$

If the breadth of the plate had been c centimeters instead of π centimeters it is easy to see that we should have needed the development of unity in a series of the form

$$A_1 \sin \frac{\pi x}{c} + A_2 \sin \frac{2\pi x}{c} + A_3 \sin \frac{3\pi x}{c} + \dots$$

Prob. 1. An iron slab 50 centimeters thick is heated to the temperature 100 degrees Centigrade throughout. The faces are then suddenly cooled to zero degrees, and are kept at that temperature for 10 minutes. Find the temperature of a point in the middle of the slab, and of a point 10 centimeters from a face at the end of that time. Assume that

$$1 = \frac{4}{\pi}\left(\sin \frac{\pi x}{c} + \frac{1}{3} \sin \frac{3\pi x}{c} + \frac{1}{5} \sin \frac{5\pi x}{c} + \dots\right) \text{ from } x = 0 \text{ to } x = c.$$

Ans. 84°.0; 49°.4.

ART. 4. PROBLEM IN ZONAL HARMONICS.

As a second example let us consider the following problem : Two equal thin hemispherical shells of radius unity placed together to form a spherical surface are separated by a thin layer of air. A charge of statical electricity is placed upon one hemisphere and the other hemisphere is connected with the ground, the first hemisphere is then found to be at potential 1, the other hemisphere being of course at potential zero. At what potential is any point in the "field of force" due to the charge?

We shall use spherical coordinates and shall let V be the potential required. Then V must satisfy equation (5), Art. 1.

But since from the symmetry of the problem V is obviously independent of ϕ, if we take the diameter perpendicular to the plane separating the two conductors as our polar axis, $\dfrac{\partial^2 V}{\partial \phi^2}$ is zero, and our equation reduces to

$$\frac{r\partial^2(rV)}{\partial r^2} + \frac{1}{\sin \theta} \frac{\partial\left(\sin \theta \dfrac{\partial V}{\partial \theta}\right)}{\partial \theta} = 0. \qquad (1)$$

V is given on the surface of our sphere, hence

$$V = f(\theta) \quad \text{when} \quad r = 1, \qquad (2)$$

where $f(\theta) = 1$ if $0 < \theta < \dfrac{\pi}{2}$, and $f(\theta) = 0$ if $\dfrac{\pi}{2} < \theta < \pi$.

Equation (2) and the implied conditions that V is zero at an infinite distance and is nowhere infinite are our conditions.

To find particular solutions of (1) we shall use a method which is generally effective. Assume* that $V = R\Theta$ where R is a function of r but not of θ, and Θ is a function of θ but not of r. Substitute in (1) and reduce, and we get

$$\frac{1}{R} \frac{r d^2(rR)}{dr^2} = - \frac{1}{\Theta \sin \theta} \frac{d\left(\sin \theta \dfrac{d\Theta}{d\theta}\right)}{d\theta}. \qquad (3)$$

Since the first member of (3) does not contain θ and the second does not contain r and the two members are identically equal, each must be equal to a constant. Let us call this constant, which is wholly undetermined, $m(m + 1)$; then

$$\frac{r}{R} \frac{d^2(rR)}{dr^2} = - \frac{1}{\Theta \sin \theta} \frac{d\left(\sin \theta \dfrac{d\Theta}{d\theta}\right)}{d\theta} = m(m + 1);$$

whence
$$r\frac{d^2(rR)}{dr^2} - m(m + 1)R = 0, \qquad (4)$$

and
$$\frac{1}{\sin \theta} \frac{d\left(\sin \theta \dfrac{d\Theta}{d\theta}\right)}{d\theta} + m(m + 1)\Theta = 0. \qquad (5)$$

* See the first foot-note on page 175.

Equation (4) can be expanded into

$$r^2 \frac{d^2R}{dr^2} + 2r \frac{dR}{dr} - m(m+1)R = 0,$$

and can be solved by elementary methods. Its complete solution is

$$R = Ar^m + Br^{-m-1}. \tag{6}$$

Equation (5) can be simplified by changing the independent variable to x where $x = \cos \theta$. It becomes

$$\frac{d}{dx}\left[(1 - x^2)\frac{d\Theta}{dx}\right] + m(m+1)\Theta = 0, \tag{7}$$

an equation which has been much studied and which is known as Legendre's Equation.

We shall restrict m, which is wholly undetermined, to positive whole values, and we can then get particular solutions of (7) by the following device:

Assume* that Θ can be expressed as a sum or a series of terms involving whole powers of x multiplied by constant coefficients.

Let $\Theta = \Sigma a_n x^n$ and substitute in (7). We get

$$\Sigma[n(n-1)a_n x^{n-2} - n(n+1)a_n x^n + m(m+1)a_n x^n] = 0, \tag{8}$$

where the symbol Σ indicates that we are to form all the terms we can by taking successive whole numbers for n.

Since (8) must be true no matter what the value of x, the coefficient of any given power of x, as for instance x^k, must vanish. Hence

$$(k+2)(k+1)a_{k+2} - k(k+1)a_k + m(m+1)a_k = 0,$$

and $$a_{k+2} = - \frac{m(m+1) - k(k+1)}{(k+1)(k+2)} a_k. \tag{9}$$

If now any set of coefficients satisfying the relation (9) be taken, $\Theta = \Sigma a_k x^k$ will be a solution of (7).

If $k = m$, then $a_{k+2} = 0$, $a_{k+4} = 0$, etc.

* See the first foot-note on page 175.

Since it will answer our purpose if we pick **out** the simplest set of coefficients that will obey the condition (9), we can take a set including a_m.

Let us rewrite (9) in the form

$$a_k = -\frac{(k+2)(k+1)a_{k+2}}{(m-k)(m+k-1)}. \tag{10}$$

We get from (10), beginning with $k = m - 2$,

$$a_{m-2} = -\frac{m(m-1)}{2.(2m-1)}a_m,$$

$$a_{m-4} = \frac{m(m-1)(m-2)(m-3)}{2.4.(2m-1)(2m-3)}a_m,$$

$$a_{m-6} = -\frac{m(m-1)(m-2)(m-3)(m-4)(m-5)}{2.4.6.(2m-1)(2m-3)(2m-5)}a_m, \text{ etc.}$$

If m is even we see that the set will end with a_0; if m is odd, with a_1.

$$\Theta = a_m\left[x^m - \frac{m(m-1)}{2.(2m-1)}x^{m-2} \right. $$
$$\left. + \frac{m(m-1)(m-2)(m-3)}{2.4.(2m-1)(2m-3)}x^{m-} - \cdots \right],$$

where a_m is entirely arbitrary, is, then, a solution of (7). It is found convenient to take a_m equal to

$$\frac{(2m-1)(2m-3)\ldots 1}{m!},$$

and it will be shown later that with this value of a_m, $\Theta = 1$ when $x = 1$.

Θ is a function of x and contains no higher powers of x than x^m. It is usual to write it as $P_m(x)$.

We proceed to write out a few values of $P_m(x)$ from the formula

$$P_m(x) = \frac{(2m-1)(2m-3)\ldots 1}{m!}\left[x^m - \frac{m(m-1)}{2.(2m-1)}x^{m-2} \right.$$
$$\left. + \frac{m(m-1)(m-2)(m-3)}{2.4.(2m-1)(2m-3)}x^{m-4} - \cdots \right] \tag{11}$$

We have:

$$
\left.
\begin{aligned}
P_0(x) &= 1 && \text{or } P_0(\cos\theta) = 1, \\
P_1(x) &= x && \text{or } P_1(\cos\theta) = \cos\theta, \\
P_2(x) &= \tfrac{1}{2}(3x^2 - 1) && \text{or } P_2(\cos\theta) = \tfrac{1}{2}(3\cos^2\theta - 1), \\
P_3(x) &= \tfrac{1}{2}(5x^3 - 3x) && \text{or } P_3(\cos\theta) = \tfrac{1}{2}(5\cos^3\theta - 3\cos\theta), \\
P_4(x) &= \tfrac{1}{8}(35x^4 - 30x^2 + 3) && \text{or} \\
&\quad P_4(\cos\theta) = \tfrac{1}{8}(35\cos^4\theta - 30\cos^2\theta + 3), \\
P_5(x) &= \tfrac{1}{8}(63x^5 - 70x^3 + 15x) && \text{or} \\
&\quad P_5(\cos\theta) = \tfrac{1}{8}(63\cos^5\theta - 70\cos^3\theta + 15\cos\theta).
\end{aligned}
\right\} \quad (12)
$$

We have obtained $\Theta = P_m(x)$ as a particular solution of (7), and $\Theta = P_m(\cos\theta)$ as a particular solution of (5). $P_m(x)$ or $P_m(\cos\theta)$ is a new function, known as a Legendre's Coefficient, or as a Surface Zonal Harmonic, and occurs as a normal form in many important problems.

$V = r^m P_m(\cos\theta)$ is a particular solution of (1), and $r^m P_m(\cos\theta)$ is sometimes called a Solid Zonal Harmonic.

$$
V = A_0 P_0(\cos\theta) + A_1 r P_1(\cos\theta) + A_2 r^2 P_2(\cos\theta) \\
+ A_3 r^3 P_3(\cos\theta) + \ldots \quad (13)
$$

satisfies (1), is not infinite at any point within the sphere, and reduces to

$$
V = A_0 P_0(\cos\theta) + A_1 P_1(\cos\theta) + A_2 P_2(\cos\theta) \\
+ A_3 P_3(\cos\theta) + \ldots \quad (14)
$$

when $r = 1$.

$$
V = \frac{A_0 P_0(\cos\theta)}{r} + \frac{A_1 P_1(\cos\theta)}{r^2} + \frac{A_2 P_2(\cos\theta)}{r^3} \\
+ \frac{A_3 P_3(\cos\theta)}{r^4} + \ldots \quad (15)
$$

satisfies (1), is not infinite at any point without the sphere, is equal to zero when $r = \infty$, and reduces to (14) when $r = 1$.

If then we can develop $f(\theta)$ [see eq. (2)] into a series of the form (14), we have only to put the coefficients of this series in place of the A_0, A_1, A_2, $\ldots$ in (13) to get the value of V for a point within the sphere, and in (15) to get the value of V at a point without the sphere.

We shall see later (Art. 16, Prob. 22) that if $f(\theta) = 1$ for $0 < \theta < \dfrac{\pi}{2}$ and $f(\theta) = 0$ for $\dfrac{\pi}{2} < \theta < \pi$,

$$f(\theta) = \frac{1}{2} + \frac{3}{4}P_1(\cos \theta) - \frac{7}{8} \cdot \frac{1}{2} \cdot P_3(\cos \theta)$$

$$+ \frac{11}{12} \cdot \frac{1 \cdot 3}{2 \cdot 4}P_5(\cos \theta) - \ldots \quad (16)$$

Hence our required solution is

$$V = \frac{1}{2} + \frac{3}{4}rP_1(\cos \theta) - \frac{7}{8} \cdot \frac{1}{2} \cdot r^3 P_3(\cos \theta)$$

$$+ \frac{11}{12} \cdot \frac{1 \cdot 3}{2 \cdot 4}r^5 P_5(\cos \theta) - \ldots \quad (17)$$

at an internal point; and

$$V = \frac{1}{2r} + \frac{3}{4} \frac{1}{r^2} P_1(\cos\theta) - \frac{7}{8} \cdot \frac{1}{2} \frac{1}{r^4} P_3(\cos \theta)$$

$$+ \frac{11}{12} \cdot \frac{1 \cdot 3}{2 \cdot 4}\frac{1}{r^6} P_5(\cos \theta) - \ldots \quad (18)$$

at an external point.

If $r = \dfrac{1}{4}$ and $\theta = 0$, (17) reduces to

$$V = \frac{1}{2} + \frac{3}{4} \cdot \frac{1}{4} - \frac{7}{8} \cdot \frac{1}{2} \cdot \frac{1}{4^3} + \frac{11}{12} \cdot \frac{1 \cdot 3}{2 \cdot 4} \cdot \frac{1}{4^5} \ldots, \text{ since } P_m(1) = 1.$$

To two decimal places $V = 0.68$, and the point $r = \dfrac{1}{4}$, $\theta = 0$ is at potential 0.68.

If $r = 5$ and $\theta = \dfrac{\pi}{4}$, (18) and Table I, at the end of this chapter, give

$$V = \frac{1}{2 \cdot 5} + \frac{3}{4} \cdot \frac{1}{5^2} \cdot 0.7071 + \frac{7}{8} \cdot \frac{1 \cdot 3}{2 \cdot 4} \cdot \frac{1}{5^4} \cdot 0.1768 + \ldots = 0.12,$$

and the point $r = 5$, $\theta = \dfrac{\pi}{4}$ is at potential 0.12.

If the radius of the conductor is a instead of unity, we have only to replace r by $\dfrac{r}{a}$ in (17) and (18).

Prob. 2. One half the surface of a solid sphere 12 inches in diameter is kept at the temperature zero and the other half at 100 degrees centigrade until there is no longer any change of temperature at any point within the sphere. Required the temperature of the center; of any point in the diametral plane separating the hot and cold hemispheres; of points 2 inches from the center and in the axis of symmetry; and of points 3 inches from the center in a diameter inclined at an angle of 45° to the axis of symmetry.

Ans. 50°; 50°; 73°.9; 26°.1; 77°.1; 22°.9.

Art. 5. Problem in Bessel's Functions.

As a last example we shall take the following problem: The base and convex surface of a cylinder 2 feet in diameter and 2 feet high are kept at the temperature zero, and the upper base at 100 degrees centigrade. Find the temperature of a point in the axis one foot from the base, and of a point 6 inches from the axis and one foot from the base, after the permanent state of temperatures has been set up.

If we use cylindrical coördinates and take the origin in the base we shall have to solve equation (6), Art. 1; or, representing the temperature by u and observing that from the symmetry of the problem u is independent of ϕ,

$$\frac{\partial^2 u}{\partial r^2} + \frac{1}{r}\frac{\partial u}{\partial r} + \frac{\partial^2 u}{\partial z^2} = 0, \tag{1}$$

subject to the conditions

$$u = 0 \quad \text{when} \quad z = 0, \tag{2}$$
$$u = 0 \quad \text{``} \quad r = 1, \tag{3}$$
$$u = 100 \quad \text{``} \quad z = 2. \tag{4}$$

Assume $u = RZ$ where R is a function of r only and Z of z only; substitute in (1) and reduce.

We get
$$\frac{1}{R}\frac{d^2 R}{dr^2} + \frac{1}{rR}\frac{dR}{dr} = -\frac{1}{Z}\frac{d^2 Z}{dz^2}. \tag{5}$$

The first member of (5) does not contain z; therefore the second member cannot. The second member of (5) does not contain r; therefore the first member cannot. Hence each member of (5) is a constant, and we can write (5)

$$\frac{1}{R}\frac{d^2R}{dr^2} + \frac{1}{rR}\frac{dR}{dr} = -\frac{1}{Z}\frac{d^2Z}{dz^2} = -\mu^2, \tag{6}$$

when μ^2 is entirely undetermined.

Hence
$$\frac{d^2Z}{dz^2} - \mu^2 Z = 0, \tag{7}$$

and
$$\frac{d^2R}{dr^2} + \frac{1}{r}\frac{dR}{dr} + \mu^2 R = 0. \tag{8}$$

Equation (7) is easily solved, and its general solution is

$$Z = Ae^{\mu z} + Be^{-\mu z}, \qquad \text{or the equivalent form}$$
$$Z = C\cosh(\mu z) + D\sinh(\mu z). \tag{9}$$

We can reduce (8) slightly by letting $\mu r = x$, and it becomes

$$\frac{d^2R}{dx^2} + \frac{1}{x}\frac{dR}{dx} + R = 0. \tag{10}$$

Assume, as in Art. 4, that R can be expressed in terms of whole powers of x. Let $R = \Sigma a_n x^n$ and substitute in (10). We get

$$\Sigma[n(n-1)a_n x^{n-2} + na_n x^{n-2} + a_n x^n] = 0,$$

an equation which must be true, no matter what the value of x. The coefficient of any given power of x, as x^{k-2}, must, then, vanish, and

$$k(k-1)a_k + ka_k + a_{k-2} = 0,$$
or
$$k^2 a_k + a_{k-2} = 0,$$
whence we obtain
$$a_{k-2} = -k^2 a_k \tag{11}$$

as the only relation that need be satisfied by the coefficients in order that $R = \Sigma a_k x^k$ shall be a solution of (10).

If $\quad k = 0, \quad a_{k-2} = 0, \quad a_{k-4} = 0, \quad$ etc.

We can, then, begin with $k = 0$ as the lowest subscript.

From (11) $a_k = -\dfrac{a_{k-2}}{k^2}$.

Then $a_2 = -\dfrac{a_0}{2^2}$, $a_4 = \dfrac{a_0}{2^2 \cdot 4^2}$, $a_6 = -\dfrac{a_0}{2^2 \cdot 4^2 \cdot 6^2}$, etc.

Hence $R = a_0 \left[1 - \dfrac{x^2}{2^2} + \dfrac{x^4}{2^2 \cdot 4^2} - \dfrac{x^6}{2^2 \cdot 4^2 \cdot 6^2} + \cdots \right]$,

where a_0 may be taken at pleasure, is a solution of (10), provided the series is convergent.

Take $a_0 = 1$, and then $R = J_0(x)$ where

$$J_0(x) = 1 - \frac{x^2}{2^2} + \frac{x^4}{2^2 \cdot 4^2} - \frac{x^6}{2^2 \cdot 4^2 \cdot 6^2} + \frac{x^8}{2^2 \cdot 4^2 \cdot 6^2 \cdot 8^2} - \cdots \quad (12)$$

is a solution of (10).

$J_0(x)$ is easily shown to be convergent for all values real or imaginary of x, it is a new and important form, and is called a Bessel's Function of the zero order, or a Cylindrical Harmonic.

Equation (10) was obtained from (8) by the substitution of $x = \mu r$; therefore

$$R = J_0(\mu r) = 1 - \frac{(\mu r)^2}{2^2} + \frac{(\mu r)^4}{2^2 \cdot 4^2} - \frac{(\mu r)^6}{2^2 \cdot 4^2 \cdot 6^2} + \cdots$$

is a solution of (8), no matter what the value of μ; and $u = J_0(\mu r) \sinh(\mu z)$ and $u = J_0(\mu r) \cosh(\mu z)$ are solutions of (1). $u = J_0(\mu r) \sinh(\mu z)$ satisfies condition (2) whatever the value of μ. In order that it should satisfy condition (3) μ must be so taken that

$$J_0(\mu) = 0; \qquad\qquad (13)$$

that is, μ must be a root of the transcendental equation (13).

It was shown by Fourier that $J_0(\mu) = 0$ has an infinite number of real positive roots, any one of which can be obtained to any required degree of approximation without serious difficulty. Let $\mu_1, \mu_2, \mu_3, \ldots$ be these roots; then

$$u = A_1 J_0(\mu_1 r) \sinh(\mu_1 z) + A_2 J_0(\mu_2 r) \sinh(\mu_2 z)$$
$$+ A_3 J_0(\mu_3 r) \sinh(\mu_3 z) + \cdots \quad (14)$$

is a solution of (1) which satisfies (2) and (3).

If now we can develop unity into a series of the form

$$1 = B_1 J_0(\mu_1 r) + B_2 J_0(\mu_2 r) + B_3 J_0(\mu_3 r) + \dots,$$

$$u = 100\left[\frac{B_1 \sinh (\mu_1 z)}{\sinh (2\mu_1)} J_0(\mu_1 r) + \frac{B_2 \sinh (\mu_2 z)}{\sinh (2\mu_2)} J_0(\mu_2 r) + \dots\right] \quad (15)$$

satisfies (1) and the conditions (2), (3), and (4).

We shall see later (Art. 21) that if $J_1(x) = -\dfrac{dJ_0(x)}{dx}$

$$1 = 2\left[\frac{J_0(\mu_1 r)}{\mu_1 J_1(\mu_1)} + \frac{J_0(\mu_2 r)}{\mu_2 J_1(\mu_2)} + \frac{J_0(\mu_3 r)}{\mu_3 J_1(\mu_3)} + \dots\right] \quad (16)$$

for values of $r < 1$.

Hence

$$u = 200\left[\frac{J_0(\mu_1 r)}{\mu_1 J_1(\mu_1)}\frac{\sinh (\mu_1 z)}{\sinh (2\mu_1)} + \frac{J_0(\mu_2 r)}{\mu_2 J_1(\mu_2)}\frac{\sinh (\mu_2 z)}{\sinh (2\mu_2)} + \dots\right] \quad (17)$$

is our required solution.

At the point $r = 0$, $z = 1$ (17) reduces to

$$u = 200\left[\frac{\sinh \mu_1}{\mu_1 J_1(\mu_1) \sinh (2\mu_1)} + \frac{\sinh \mu_2}{\mu_2 J_1(\mu_2) \sinh (2\mu_2)} + \dots\right]$$

$$= 100\left[\frac{1}{\mu_1 J_1(\mu_1) \cosh \mu_1} + \frac{1}{\mu_2 J_1(\mu_2) \cosh \mu_2} + \dots\right],$$

since $J_0(0) = 1$ and $\sinh (2x) = 2 \sinh x \cosh x$.

If we use a table of Hyperbolic functions* and Tables II and III, at the end of this chapter, the computation of the value of u is easy. We have

$\mu_1 = 2.405$	$\mu_2 = \quad 5.520$
$J_1(\mu_1) = 0.5190$	$J_1(\mu_2) = -0.3402$
colog $\mu_1 = 9.6189 - 10$	colog $\mu_2 = \quad 9.2581 \quad - 10$
" $J_1(\mu_1) = 0.2848$	" $J_1(\mu_2) = \quad 0.4683n$
" $\cosh \mu_1 = 9.2530 - 10$	" $\cosh \mu_2 = \quad 7.9037 \quad - 10$
$9.1567 - 10$	$7.6301n - 10$

* See Chapter IV, pp. 162, 163, for a four-place table on hyperbolic functions.

$$(\mu_1 J_1(\mu_1) \cosh \mu_1)^{-1} = \quad 0.1434$$
$$(\mu_2 J_1(\mu_2) \cosh \mu_2)^{-1} = - 0.0058$$

$$0.1376; \qquad u = 13°.8$$

At the point $r = \frac{1}{2}$, $z = 1$, (17), reduces to

$$u = 100\left[\frac{J_0(\frac{1}{2}\mu_1)}{\mu_1 J_1(\mu_1) \cosh \mu_1} + \frac{J_0(\frac{1}{2}\mu_2)}{\mu_2 J_1(\mu_2) \cosh \mu_2} + \cdots\right].$$

$$J_0(\tfrac{1}{2}\mu_1) = 0.6698$$

$$\log J_0(\tfrac{1}{2}\mu_1) = 9.8259 \quad - 10$$
$$\text{colog } \mu_1 J_1(\mu_1) \cosh \mu_1 = 9.1567 \quad - 10$$

$$8.9826 \quad - 10;$$

$$J_0(\tfrac{1}{2}\mu_2) = - 0.1678$$

$$\log J_0(\tfrac{1}{2}\mu_2) = \quad 9.2248n - 10$$
$$\text{colog } \mu_2 J_1(\mu_2) \cosh \mu_2 = \quad 7.6301n - 10$$

$$6.8549 \quad - 10;$$

$$\frac{J_0(\tfrac{1}{2}\mu_1)}{\mu_1 J_1(\mu_1) \cosh \mu_1} = 0.0961$$

$$\frac{J_0(\tfrac{1}{2}\mu_2)}{\mu_2 J_1(\mu_2) \cosh \mu_2} = \frac{0.0007}{0.0968}; \qquad u = 9°.7$$

If the radius of the cylinder is a and the altitude b, we have only to replace μ by μa in (13); $2\mu_1$, $2\mu_2$, ... in the denominators of (15) and (17) by $\mu_1 b$, $\mu_2 b$, ...; and μ_1, μ_2, μ_3, ... in the denominators of (16) and (17) by $\mu_1 a$, $\mu_2 a$, $\mu_3 a$, ...

Prob. 3. One base and the convex surface of a cylinder 20 centimeters in diameter and 30 centimeters high are kept at zero temperature and the other base at 100 degrees Centigrade. Find the temperature of a point in the axis and 20 centimeters from the cold base, and of a point 5 centimeters from the axis and 20 centimeters from the cold base after the temperatures have ceased to change.

Ans. $13°.9$; $9°.6$.

ART. 6. THE SINE SERIES.

As we have seen in Art. 3, it is sometimes important to be able to express a given function of a variable, x, in terms of sines of multiples of x. The problem in its general form was first solved by Fourier in his " Théorie Analytique de la Chaleur" (1822), and its solution plays an important part in most branches of Mathematical Physics.

Let us endeavor to so develop a given function of x, $f(x)$, in terms of sin x, sin $2x$, sin $3x$, etc., that the function and the series shall be equal for all values of x between 0 and π.

We can of course determine the coefficients $a_1, a_2, a_3, \ldots a_n$ so that the equation

$$f(x) = a_1 \sin x + a_2 \sin 2x + a_3 \sin 3x + \ldots + a_n \sin nx \quad (1)$$

shall hold good for any n arbitrarily chosen values of x between 0 and π; for we have only to substitute those values in turn in (1) to get n equations of the first degree, in which the n coefficients are the only unknown quantities.

For instance, we can take the n equidistant values Δx, $2\Delta x$, $3\Delta x$, $\ldots n\Delta x$, where $\Delta x = \dfrac{\pi}{n+1}$, and substitute them for x in (1). We get

$$
\left.
\begin{aligned}
f(\Delta x) &= a_1 \sin \Delta x + a_2 \sin 2\Delta x + a_3 \sin 3\Delta x + \ldots \\
&\qquad\qquad + a_n \sin n\Delta x, \\
f(2\Delta x) &= a_1 \sin 2\Delta x + a_2 \sin 4\Delta x + a_3 \sin 6\Delta x + \ldots \\
&\qquad\qquad + a_n \sin 2n\Delta x, \\
f(3\Delta x) &= a_1 \sin 3\Delta x + a_2 \sin 6\Delta x + a_3 \sin 9\Delta x + \ldots \\
&\qquad\qquad + a_n \sin 3n\Delta x, \\
&\;\;\vdots \qquad\qquad \vdots \qquad\qquad \vdots \\
f(n\Delta x) &= a_1 \sin n\Delta x + a_2 \sin 2n\Delta x + a_3 \sin 3n\Delta x + \ldots \\
&\qquad\qquad + a_n \sin n^2\Delta x,
\end{aligned}
\right\} \quad (2)
$$

n equations of the first degree, to determine the n coefficients $a_1, a_2, a_3, \ldots a_n$.

Not only can equations (2) be solved in theory, but they can be actually solved in any given case by a very simple and ingenious method due to Lagrange,* and any coefficient a_m can be expressed in the form

$$a_m = \frac{2}{n+1} \sum_{\kappa=1}^{\kappa=n} f(\kappa \Delta x) \sin (\kappa m \Delta x). \tag{3}$$

If now n is indefinitely increased the values of x for which (1) holds good will come nearer and nearer to forming a continuous set; and the limiting value approached by a_m will probably be the corresponding coefficient in the series required to represent $f(x)$ for all values of x between zero and π.

Remembering that $(n+1)\Delta x = \pi$, the limiting value in question is easily seen to be

$$a_m = \frac{2}{\pi} \int_0^\pi f(x) \sin mx\, dx. \tag{4}$$

This value can be obtained from equations (2) by the following device without first solving the equations:

Let us multiply each equation in (2) by the product of Δx and the coefficient of a_m in the equation in question, add the equations, and find the limiting form of the resulting equation as n increases indefinitely.

The coefficient of any a, a_κ in the resulting equation is

$$\sin \kappa \Delta x \sin m \Delta x . \Delta x + \sin 2\kappa \Delta x \sin 2m \Delta x . \Delta x + \ldots$$
$$+ \sin n\kappa \Delta x \sin nm \Delta x . \Delta x.$$

Its limiting value, since $(n+1)\Delta x = \pi$, is

$$\int_0^\pi \sin \kappa x \sin mx . dx;$$

but

$$\int_0^\pi \sin \kappa x \sin mx . dx = \tfrac{1}{2} \int_0^\pi [\cos (m - \kappa)x - \cos(m + \kappa)x] dx = 0$$

if m and κ are not equal.

---

* See Riemann's Partielle Differentialgleichungen, or Byerly's Fourier's Series and Spherical Harmonics.

The coefficient of a_m is

$$\Delta x(\sin^2 m\Delta x + \sin^2 2m\Delta x + \sin^2 3m\Delta x + \ldots + \sin^2 nm\Delta x).$$

Its limiting value is

$$\int_0^\pi \sin^2 mx \,.\, dx = \frac{\pi}{2}.$$

The first member is

$$f(\Delta x) \sin m\Delta x \,.\, \Delta x + f(2\Delta x) \sin 2m\Delta x \,.\, \Delta x + \ldots$$
$$+ f(n\Delta x) \sin mn\Delta x \,.\, \Delta x,$$

and its limiting value is

$$\int_0^\pi f(x) \sin mx \,.\, dx.$$

Hence the limiting form approached by the final equation as n is increased is

$$\int_0^\pi f(x) \sin mx \,.\, dx = \frac{\pi}{2} a_m.$$

Whence $\qquad a_m = \dfrac{2}{\pi} \displaystyle\int_0^\pi f(x) \sin mx \,.\, dx \qquad\qquad (5)$

as before.

This method is practically the same as multiplying the equation

$$f(x) = a_1 \sin x + a_2 \sin 2x + a_3 \sin 3x + \ldots \qquad (6)$$

by $\sin mx \,.\, dx$ and integrating both members from zero to π.

It is important to realize that the considerations given in this article are in no sense a demonstration, but merely establish a probability.

An elaborate investigation [*] into the validity of the development, for which we have not space, entirely confirms the results formulated above, provided that between $x = 0$ and $x = \pi$ the

[*] See Art. 10 for a discussion of this question.

function is finite and single-valued, and has not an infinite number of discontinuities or of maxima or minima.

It is to be noted that the curve represented by $y = f(x)$ need not follow the same mathematical law throughout its length, but may be made up of portions of entirely different curves. For example, a broken line or a locus consisting of finite parts of several different and disconnected straight lines can be represented perfectly well by $y =$ a sine series.

As an example of the application of formula (5) let us take the development of unity.

Here $$f(x) = 1.$$

$$a_m = \frac{2}{\pi} \int_0^\pi \sin mx \,.\, dx \,;$$

$$\int \sin mx \,.\, dx = -\frac{\cos mx}{m}.$$

$$\int_0^\pi \sin mx \,.\, dx = \frac{1}{m}(1 - \cos m\pi) = \frac{1}{m}[1 - (-1)^m]$$

$$= 0 \text{ if } m \text{ is even}$$

$$= \frac{2}{m} \text{ if } m \text{ is odd.}$$

Hence $$1 = \frac{4}{\pi}\left(\frac{\sin x}{1} + \frac{\sin 3x}{3} + \frac{\sin 5x}{5} + \frac{\sin 7x}{7} + \cdots\right). \quad (7)$$

It is to be noticed that (7) gives at once a sine development for any constant c. It is,

$$c = \frac{4c}{\pi}\left(\frac{\sin x}{1} + \frac{\sin 3x}{3} + \frac{\sin 5x}{5} + \cdots\right). \quad (8)$$

Prob. 4. Show that for values of x between zero and π

(a) $$x = 2\left[\frac{\sin x}{1} - \frac{\sin 2x}{2} + \frac{\sin 3x}{3} - \frac{\sin 4x}{4} + \cdots\right],$$

(b) $$f(x) = \frac{4}{\pi}\left[\frac{\sin x}{1^2} - \frac{\sin 3x}{3^2} + \frac{\sin 5x}{5^2} - \frac{\sin 7x}{7^2} + \cdots\right]$$

if $f(x) = x$ for $0 < x < \dfrac{\pi}{2}$, and $f(x) = \pi - x$ for $\dfrac{\pi}{2} < x < \pi$.

(c) $f(x) =$

$$\frac{2}{\pi}\left[\frac{\sin x}{1} + \frac{2\sin 2x}{2} + \frac{\sin 3x}{3} + \frac{\sin 5x}{5} + \frac{2\sin 6x}{6} + \frac{\sin 7x}{7} + \ldots\right]$$

if $f(x) = 1$ for $0 < x < \dfrac{\pi}{2}$, and $f(x) = 0$ for $\dfrac{\pi}{2} < x < \pi$.

(d) $\sinh x =$

$$\frac{2\sinh \pi}{\pi}\left[\frac{1}{2}\sin x - \frac{2}{5}\sin 2x + \frac{3}{10}\sin 3x - \frac{4}{17}\sin 4x + \ldots\right].$$

(e) $x^2 =$

$$\frac{2}{\pi}\left[\left(\frac{\pi^2}{1} - \frac{4}{1^3}\right)\sin x - \frac{\pi^2}{2}\sin 2x + \left(\frac{\pi^2}{3} - \frac{4}{3^3}\right)\sin 3x - \frac{\pi^2}{4}\sin 4x + \ldots\right].$$

ART. 7.　THE COSINE SERIES.

Let us now try to develop a given function of x in a series of cosines, using the method suggested by the last article.

Assume

$$f(x) = b_0 + b_1 \cos x + b_2 \cos 2x + b_3 \cos 3x + \ldots \tag{1}$$

To determine any coefficient b_m multiply (1) by $\cos mx \,.\, dx$ and integrate each term from 0 to π.

$$\int_0^\pi b_0 \cos mx \,.\, dx = 0.$$

$$\int_0^\pi b_k \cos kx \cos mx \,.\, dx = 0, \quad \text{if } m \text{ and } k \text{ are not equal.}$$

$$\int_0^\pi b_m \cos^2 mx \; dx = \frac{\pi}{2}b_m, \quad \text{if } m \text{ is not zero.}$$

Hence $b_m = \dfrac{2}{\pi}\displaystyle\int_0^\pi f(x) \cos mx \,.\, dx,$ 　　　　(2)

if m is not zero.

To get b_0 multiply (1) by dx and integrate from zero to π.

$$\int_0^\pi b_0 dx = b_0 \pi,$$

$$\int_0^\pi b_k \cos kx . dx = 0.$$

Hence $$b_0 = \frac{1}{\pi} \int_0^\pi f(x)dx, \tag{3}$$

which is just half the value that would be given by formula (2) if zero were substituted for m.

To save a separate formula (1) is usually written

$$f(x) = \tfrac{1}{2}b_0 + b_1 \cos x + b_2 \cos 2x + b_3 \cos 3x + \ldots, \tag{4}$$

and then the formula (2) will give b_0 as well as the other coefficients.

Prob. 5. Show that for values of x between o and π

(a) $x = \dfrac{\pi}{2} - \dfrac{4}{\pi}\left(\dfrac{\cos x}{1^2} + \dfrac{\cos 3x}{3^2} + \dfrac{\cos 5x}{5^2} + \ldots\right);$

(b) $f(x) = \dfrac{\pi}{4} - \dfrac{8}{\pi}\left(\dfrac{\cos 2x}{2^2} + \dfrac{\cos 6x}{6^2} + \dfrac{\cos 10x}{10^2} + \ldots\right),$

if $f(x) = x$ for $0 < x < \dfrac{\pi}{2}$, and $f(x) = \pi - x$ for $\dfrac{\pi}{2} < x < \pi$;

(c) $f(x) = \dfrac{1}{2} + \dfrac{2}{\pi}\left(\dfrac{\cos x}{1} - \dfrac{\cos 3x}{3} + \dfrac{\cos 5x}{5} - \ldots\right),$

if $f(x) = 1$ for $0 < x < \dfrac{\pi}{2}$, and $f(x) = 0$ for $\dfrac{\pi}{2} < x < \pi$,

(d) $\sinh x = \dfrac{2}{\pi}\left[\dfrac{1}{2}(\cosh \pi - 1) - \dfrac{1}{2}(\cosh \pi + 1) \cos x\right.$

$\left. + \dfrac{1}{5}(\cosh \pi - 1) \cos 2x - \dfrac{1}{10}(\cosh \pi + 1) \cos 3x + \ldots\right];$

(e) $x^2 = \dfrac{\pi^2}{3} - 4\left(\dfrac{\cos x}{1^2} - \dfrac{\cos 2x}{2^2} + \dfrac{\cos 3x}{3^2} - \dfrac{\cos 4x}{4^2} + \ldots\right).$

ART. 8.　FOURIER'S SERIES.

Since a sine series is an odd function of x the development
of an odd function of x in such a series must hold good from
$x = - \pi$ to $x = \pi$, except perhaps for the value $x = 0$, where
it is easily seen that the series is necessarily zero, no matter
what the value of the function.　In like manner we see that
if $f(x)$ is an even function of x its development in a cosine
series must be valid from $x = - \pi$ to $x = \pi$.

Any function of x can be developed into a Trigonometric
series to which it is equal for all values of x between $- \pi$ and π.

Let $f(x)$ be the given function of x.　It can be expressed
as the sum of an even function of x and an odd function of x
by the following device :

$$f(x) = \frac{f(x) + f(- x)}{2} + \frac{f(x) - f(- x)}{2} \qquad (1)$$

identically; but $\dfrac{f(x) + f(- x)}{2}$ is not changed by reversing
the sign of x and is therefore an even function of x; and when
we reverse the sign of x, $\dfrac{f(x) - f(- x)}{2}$ is affected only to the
extent of having its sign reversed, and is consequently an odd
function of x.

Therefore for all values of x between $- \pi$ and π

$$\frac{f(x) + f(- x)}{2} = \frac{1}{2}b_0 + b_1 \cos x + b_2 \cos 2x + b_3 \cos 3x + \ldots$$

where $\qquad b_m = \dfrac{2}{\pi} \displaystyle\int_0^\pi \dfrac{f(x) + f(- x)}{2} \cos mx \, . \, dx$;

and $\qquad \dfrac{f(x) - f(- x)}{2} = a_1 \sin x + a_2 \sin 2x + a_3 \sin 3x + \ldots$

where $\qquad a_m = \dfrac{2}{\pi} \displaystyle\int_0^\pi \dfrac{f(x) - f(- x)}{2} \sin mx \, . \, dx$.

b_m and a_m can be simplified a little.

$$b_m = \frac{2}{\pi} \int_0^\pi \frac{f(x) + f(-x)}{2} \cos mx \, . \, dx$$

$$= \frac{1}{\pi} \left[\int_0^\pi f(x) \cos mx \, . \, dx + \int_0^\pi f(-x) \cos mx \, . \, dx \right];$$

but if we replace x by $-x$, we get

$$\int_0^\pi f(-x) \cos mx \, . \, dx = -\int_0^{-\pi} f(x) \cos mx \, . \, dx = \int_{-\pi}^0 f(x) \cos mx \, . \, dx,$$

and we have $\qquad b_m = \dfrac{1}{\pi} \int_{-\pi}^\pi f(x) \cos mx \, . \, dx.$

In the same way we can reduce the value of a_m to

$$\frac{1}{\pi} \int_{-\pi}^\pi f(x) \sin mx \, . \, dx.$$

Hence

$$f(x) = \frac{1}{2} b_0 + b_1 \cos x + b_2 \cos 2x + b_3 \cos 3x + \dots$$

$$+ a_1 \sin x + a_2 \sin 2x + a_3 \sin 3x + \dots, \quad (2)$$

where $\qquad b_m = \dfrac{1}{\pi} \int_{-\pi}^\pi f(x) \cos mx \, . \, dx, \qquad\qquad (3)$

and $\qquad a_m = \dfrac{1}{\pi} \int_{-\pi}^\pi f(x) \sin mx \, . \, dx, \qquad\qquad (4)$

and this development holds for all values of x between $-\pi$ and π.

The second member of (2) is known as a Fourier's Series.

The developments of Arts. 5 and 7 are special cases of development in Fourier's Series.

Prob. 6. Show that for all values of x from $-\pi$ to π

$$e^x = \frac{2 \sinh \pi}{\pi} \left[\frac{1}{2} - \frac{1}{2} \cos x + \frac{1}{5} \cos 2x - \frac{1}{10} \cos 3x + \frac{1}{17} \cos 4x + \dots \right]$$

$$+ \frac{2 \sinh \pi}{\pi} \left[\frac{1}{2} \sin x - \frac{2}{5} \sin 2x + \frac{3}{10} \sin 3x - \frac{4}{17} \sin 4x + \ldots \right].$$

Prob. 7. Show that formula (2), Art. 8, can be written

$$f(x) = \frac{1}{2} c_0 \cos \beta_0 + c_1 \cos (x - \beta_1) + c_2 \cos (2x - \beta_2)$$
$$+ c_3 \cos (3x - \beta_3) + \ldots,$$

where $\quad c_m = (a_m{}^2 + b_m{}^2)^{\frac{1}{2}} \quad$ and $\quad \beta_m = \tan^{-1} \dfrac{a_m}{b_m}.$

Prob. 8. Show that formula (2), Art. 8, can be written

$$f(x) = \frac{1}{2} c_0 \sin \beta_0 + c_1 \sin (x + \beta_1) + c_2 \sin (2x + \beta_2)$$
$$+ c_3 \sin (3x + \beta_3) + \ldots,$$

where $\quad c_m = (a_m{}^2 + b_m{}^2)^{\frac{1}{2}} \quad$ and $\quad \beta_m = \tan^{-1} \dfrac{b_m}{a_m}.$

ART. 9. EXTENSION OF FOURIER'S SERIES.

In developing a function of x into a Trigonometric Series it is often inconvenient to be held within the narrow boundaries $x = - \pi$ and $x = \pi$. Let us see if we cannot widen them.

Let it be required to develop a function of x into a Trigonometric Series which shall be equal to $f(x)$ for all values of x between $x = - c$ and $x = c$.

Introduce a new variable

$$z = \frac{\pi}{c} x,$$

which is equal to $- \pi$ when $x = - c$, and to π when $x = c$.

$f(x) = f\left(\dfrac{c}{\pi} z \right)$ can be developed in terms of z by Art. 8, (2), (3), and (4). We have

$$f\left(\frac{c}{\pi} z \right) = \frac{1}{2} b_0 + b_1 \cos z + b_2 \cos 2z + b_3 \cos 3z + \ldots$$
$$+ a_1 \sin z + a_2 \sin 2z + a_3 \sin 3z + \ldots, \quad (1)$$

where $\qquad b_m = \dfrac{1}{\pi} \displaystyle\int_{-\pi}^{\pi} f\left(\dfrac{c}{\pi} z \right) \cos mz \, . \, dz, \qquad (2)$

and
$$a_m = \frac{1}{\pi} \int_{-\pi}^{\pi} f\left(\frac{c}{\pi}z\right) \sin mz \cdot dz, \tag{3}$$

and (1) holds good from $z = -\pi$ to $z = \pi$.

Replace z by its value in terms of x and (1) becomes

$$f(x) = \frac{1}{2} b_0 + b_1 \cos \frac{\pi x}{c} + b_2 \cos \frac{2\pi x}{c} + b_3 \cos \frac{3\pi x}{c} + \cdots$$

$$+ a_1 \sin \frac{\pi x}{c} + a_2 \sin \frac{2\pi x}{c} + a_3 \sin \frac{3\pi x}{c} + \cdots; \tag{4}$$

and (2) and (3) can be transformed into

$$b_m = \frac{1}{c} \int_{-c}^{c} f(x) \cos \frac{m\pi x}{c} dx, \tag{5}$$

$$a_m = \frac{1}{c} \int_{-c}^{c} f(x) \sin \frac{m\pi x}{c} dx, \tag{6}$$

and (4) holds good from $x = -c$ to $x = c$.

In the formulas just obtained c may have as great a value as we please so that we can obtain a Trigonometric Series for $f(x)$ that will be equal to the given function through as great an interval as we may choose to take.

It can be shown that if this interval c is increased indefinitely the series will approach as its limiting form the double integral $\frac{1}{\pi} \int_{-\infty}^{\infty} f(\lambda) d\lambda \int_{0}^{\infty} \cos \alpha(\lambda - x) d\alpha$, which is known as a Fourier's Integral. So that

$$f(x) = \frac{1}{\pi} \int_{-\infty}^{+\infty} f(\lambda) d\lambda \int_{0}^{\infty} \cos \alpha(\lambda - x) d\alpha \tag{7}$$

for all values of x.

For the treatment of Fourier's Integral and for examples of its use in Mathematical Physics the student is referred to Riemann's Partielle Differentialgleichungen, to Schlömilch's Höhere Analysis, and to Byerly's Fourier's Series and Spherical Harmonics.

Prob. 9. Show that formula (4), Art. 9, can be written

$$f(x) = \frac{1}{2} c_0 \cos \beta_0 + c_1 \cos \left(\frac{\pi x}{c} - \beta_1 \right) + c_2 \cos \left(\frac{2\pi x}{c} - \beta_2 \right)$$

$$+ c_3 \cos \left(\frac{3\pi x}{c} - \beta_3 \right) + \ldots,$$

where $c_m = (a_m{}^2 + b_m{}^2)^{\frac{1}{2}}$ and $\beta_m = \tan^{-1} \frac{a_m}{b_m}$.

Prob. 10. Show that formula (4), Art. 9, can be written

$$f(x) = \frac{1}{2} c_0 \sin \beta_0 + c_1 \sin \left(\frac{\pi x}{c} + \beta_1 \right) + c_2 \sin \left(\frac{2\pi x}{c} + \beta_2 \right)$$

$$+ c_3 \sin \left(\frac{3\pi x}{c} + \beta_3 \right) + \ldots,$$

where $c_m = (a_m{}^2 + b_m{}^2)^{\frac{1}{2}}$ and $\beta_m = \tan^{-1} \frac{b_m}{a_m}$.

ART. 10. DIRICHLET'S CONDITIONS.

In determining the coefficients of the Fourier's Series representing $f(x)$ we have virtually assumed, first, that a series of the required form and equal to $f(x)$ exists; and second, that it is *uniformly convergent;* and consequently we must regard the results obtained as only provisionally established.

It is, however, possible to prove rigorously that if $f(x)$ is finite and single-valued from $x = -\pi$ to $x = \pi$ and has not an infinite number of (finite) discontinuities, or of maxima or minima between $x = -\pi$ and $x = \pi$, the Fourier's Series of (2), Art. 8, and that Fourier's Series only, is equal to $f(x)$ for all values of x between $-\pi$ and π, excepting the values of x corresponding to the discontinuities of $f(x)$, and the values π and $-\pi$; and that if c is a value of x corresponding to a discontinuity of $f(x)$, the value of the series when $x = c$ is $\frac{1}{2} \underset{\epsilon = 0}{\text{limit}} [f(c + \epsilon) + f(c - \epsilon)]$; and that when $x = \pi$ or $x = -\pi$ the value of the series is $\frac{1}{2}[f(\pi) + f(-\pi)]$.

This proof was first given by Dirichlet in 1829, and may be found in readable form in Riemann's Partielle Differentialgleichungen and in Picard's Traité d'Analyse, Vol. I.

A good deal of light is thrown on the peculiarities of trigo-nometric series by the attempt to construct approximately the curves corresponding to them.

If we construct $y = a_1 \sin x$ and $y = a_2 \sin 2x$ and add the ordinates of the points having the same abscissas, we shall ob-tain points on the curve

$$y = a_1 \sin x + a_2 \sin 2x.$$

If now we construct $y = a_3 \sin 3x$ and add the ordinates to those of $y = a_1 \sin x + a_2 \sin 2x$ we shall get the curve

$$y = a_1 \sin x + a_2 \sin 2x + a_3 \sin 3x.$$

By continuing this process we get successive approximations to

$$y = a_1 \sin x + a_2 \sin 2x + a_3 \sin 3x + a_4 \sin 4x + \cdots$$

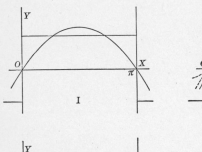

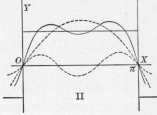

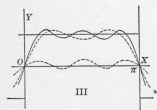

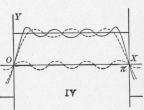

Let us apply this method to the series

$$y = \sin x + \tfrac{1}{3}\sin 3x + \tfrac{1}{5}\sin 5x + \cdots \qquad (1) \text{ (See (7), Art. 6.)}$$

$y = 0$ when $x = 0$, $\dfrac{\pi}{4}$ from $x = 0$ to $x = \pi$, and 0 when $x = \pi$.

It must be borne in mind that our curve is periodic, hav-ing the period 2π, and is symmetrical with respect to the origin.

The preceding figures represent the first four approximation to this curve. In each figure the curve $y =$ the series, and the approximations in question are drawn in continuous lines, and the preceding approximation and the curve corresponding to the term to be added are drawn in dotted lines.

Prob. 11. Construct successive approximations to the series given in the examples at the end of Art. 6.

Prob. 12. Construct successive approximations to the Maclaurin's Series for sinh x, namely $x + \dfrac{x^3}{3!} + \dfrac{x^5}{5!} + \cdots$

Art. 11. Applications of Trigonometric Series.

(*a*) Three edges of a rectangular plate of tinfoil are kept at potential zero, and the fourth at potential 1. At what potential is any point in the plate?

Here we have to solve Laplace's Equation (3), Art. 1, which, since the problem is two-dimensional, reduces to

$$\frac{\partial^2 V}{\partial x^2} + \frac{\partial^2 V}{\partial y^2} = 0, \tag{1}$$

subject to the conditions $V = 0$ when $x = 0$,   (2)

$$V = 0 \text{ “ } \quad x = a, \tag{3}$$
$$V = 0 \text{ “ } \quad y = 0, \tag{4}$$
$$V = 1 \text{ “ } \quad y = b. \tag{5}$$

Working as in Art. 3, we readily get $\sinh \beta y \, \sin \beta x$, $\sinh \beta y \, \cos \beta x$, $\cosh \beta y \, \sin \beta x$, and $\cosh \beta y \, \cos \beta x$ as particular values of V satisfying (1).

$V = \sinh \dfrac{m\pi y}{a} \sin \dfrac{m\pi x}{a}$ satisfies (1), (2), (3), and (4).

$$V = \frac{4}{\pi} \left[\frac{\sinh \dfrac{\pi y}{a}}{\sinh \dfrac{\pi b}{a}} \sin \frac{\pi x}{a} + \frac{1}{3} \frac{\sinh \dfrac{3\pi y}{a}}{\sinh \dfrac{3\pi b}{a}} \sin \frac{3\pi x}{a} + \cdots \right] \tag{6}$$

is the required solution, for it reduces to 1 when $y = b$. See (7), Art. 6.

(*b*) A harp-string is initially distorted into a given plane curve and then released; find its motion.

The differential equation for the small transverse vibrations of a stretched elastic string is

$$\frac{\partial^2 y}{\partial t^2} = a^2 \frac{\partial^2 y}{\partial x^2}, \tag{1}$$

as stated in Art. 1. Our conditions if we take one end of the string as origin are

$$y = 0 \text{ when } x = 0, \tag{2}$$
$$y = 0 \quad \text{``} \quad x = l, \tag{3}$$
$$\frac{\partial y}{\partial t} = 0 \quad \text{``} \quad t = 0, \tag{4}$$
$$y = fx \quad \text{``} \quad t = 0. \tag{5}$$

Using the method of Art. 3, we easily get as particular solutions of (1)

$$y = \sin \beta x \sin a\beta t, \qquad y = \sin \beta x \cos a\beta t,$$
$$y = \cos \beta x \sin a\beta t, \quad \text{and} \quad y = \cos \beta x \cos a\beta t.$$

$$y = \sin \frac{m\pi x}{l} \cos \frac{m\pi a t}{l} \text{ satisfies (1), (2), (3), and (4).}$$

$$y = \sum_{m=1}^{m=\infty} a_m \sin \frac{m\pi x}{l} \cos \frac{m\pi a t}{l}, \tag{6}$$

where $\qquad a_m = \dfrac{2}{l} \displaystyle\int_0^l f(x) \sin \dfrac{m\pi x}{l} . dx \tag{7}$

is our required solution; for it reduces to $f(x)$ when $t = 0$. See Art. 9.

Prob. 13. Three edges of a square sheet of tinfoil are kept at potential zero, and the fourth at potential unity; at what potential is the centre of the sheet? Ans. 0.25.

Prob. 14. Two opposite edges of a square sheet of tinfoil are kept at potential zero, and the other two at potential unity; at what potential is the centre of the sheet? Ans. 0.5.

Prob. 15. Two adjacent edges of a square sheet of tinfoil are kept at potential zero, and the other two at potential unity. At what potential is the centre of the sheet? Ans. 0.5.

Prob. 16. Show that if a point whose distance from the end of a harp-string is $\frac{1}{n}$-th the length of the string is drawn aside by the player's finger to a distance b from its position of equilibrium and then released, the form of the vibrating string at any instant is given by the equation

$$y = \frac{2bn^2}{(n-1)\pi^2} \sum_{m=1}^{m=\infty} \left(\frac{1}{m^2} \sin \frac{m\pi}{n} \sin \frac{m\pi x}{l} \cos \frac{m\pi at}{l} \right).$$

Show from this that all the harmonics of the fundamental note of the string which correspond to forms of vibration having nodes at the point drawn aside by the finger will be wanting in the complex note actually sounded.

Prob. 17.* An iron slab 10 centimeters thick is placed between and in contact with two other iron slabs each 10 centimeters thick. The temperature of the middle slab is at first 100 degrees Centigrade throughout, and of the outside slabs zero throughout. The outer faces of the outside slabs are kept at the temperature zero. Required the temperature of a point in the middle of the middle slab fifteen minutes after the slabs have been placed in contact. Given $a^2 = 0.185$ in C.G.S. units. Ans. $10°.3$.

Prob. 18.* Two iron slabs each 20 centimeters thick, one of which is at the temperature zero and the other at 100 degrees Centigrade throughout, are placed together face to face, and their outer faces are kept at the temperature zero. Find the temperature of a point in their common face and of points 10 centimeters from the common face fifteen minutes after the slabs have been put together. Ans. $22°.8$; $15°.1$; $17°.2$.

ART. 12.† PROPERTIES OF ZONAL HARMONICS.

In Art. 4, $z = P_m(x)$ was obtained as a particular solution of Legendre's Equation [(7), Art. 4] by the device of assuming that z could be expressed as a sum or a series of terms of the form $a_n x^n$ and then determining the coefficients. We

* See Art. 3.
† The student should review Art. 4 before beginning this article.

can, however, obtain a particular solution of Legendre's equation by an entirely different method.

The potential function for any point (x, y, z) due to a unit of mass concentrated at a given point (x_1, y_1, z_1) is

$$V = \frac{1}{\sqrt{(x - x_1)^2 + (y - y_1)^2 + (z - z_1)^2}}, \tag{1}$$

and this must be a particular solution of Laplace's Equation [(3), Art. 1], as is easily verified by direct substitution.

If we transform (1) to spherical coordinates we get

$$V = \frac{1}{\sqrt{r^2 - 2rr_1[\cos \theta \cos \theta_1 + \sin \theta \sin \theta_1 \cos (\phi - \phi_1)] + r_1^2}} \tag{2}$$

as a solution of Laplace's Equation in Spherical Coordinates [(5), Art. 1].

If the given point (x_1, y_1, z_1) is taken on the axis of X, as it must be in order that (2) may be independent of ϕ, $\theta_1 = 0$, and

$$V = \frac{1}{\sqrt{r^2 - 2rr_1 \cos \theta + r_1^2}} \tag{3}$$

is a solution of equation (1), Art. 4.

Equation (3) can be written

$$V = \frac{1}{r_1}\left(1 - 2\frac{r}{r_1} \cos \theta + \frac{r^2}{r_1^2}\right)^{-\frac{1}{2}}; \tag{4}$$

and if r is less than r_1 $\left(1 - 2\dfrac{r}{r_1} \cos \theta + \dfrac{r^2}{r_1^2}\right)^{-\frac{1}{2}}$ can be developed into a convergent power series. Let $\Sigma p_m \dfrac{r^m}{r_1^m}$ be this series, p_m being of course a function of θ. Then $V = \dfrac{1}{r_1}\Sigma p_m \dfrac{r^m}{r_1^m}$ is a solution of (1), Art. 4.

Substituting this value of V in the equation, and remembering that the result must be identically true, we get after a slight reduction

$$m(m + 1)p_m + \frac{1}{\sin \theta} \frac{d}{d\theta}\left[\sin \theta \frac{dp_m}{d\theta}\right] = 0;$$

but, as we have seen, the substitution of $x = \cos \theta$ reduces this to Legendre's equation [(7), Art. 4]. Hence we infer that the coefficient of the mth power of z in the development of $(1 - 2xz + z^2)^{-\frac{1}{2}}$ is a function of x that will satisfy Legendre's equation.

$$(1 - 2xz + z^2)^{-\frac{1}{2}} = [1 - z(2x - z)]^{-\frac{1}{2}},$$

and can be developed by the Binomial Theorem; the coefficient of z^m is easily picked out, and proves to be precisely the function of x which in Art. 4 we have represented by $P_m(x)$, and have called a Surface Zonal Harmonic.

We have, then,

$$(1 - 2xz + z^2)^{-\frac{1}{2}} = P_0(x) + P_1(x) \cdot z + P_2(x) \cdot z^2 + P_3(x) \cdot z^3 + \ldots \quad (5)$$

if the absolute value of z is less than 1.

If $x = 1$, (5) reduces to

$$(1 - 2z + z^2)^{-\frac{1}{2}} = P_0(1) + P_1(1) \cdot z + P_2(1) \cdot z^2 + P_3(1) \cdot z^3 + \ldots;$$

but $\quad (1 - 2z + z^2)^{-\frac{1}{2}} = (1 - z)^{-1} = 1 + z + z^2 + z^3 + \ldots;$

hence $\qquad\qquad P_m(1) = 1.$ $\qquad\qquad$ (6)

Any Surface Zonal Harmonic may be obtained from the two of next lower orders by the aid of the formula

$$(n + 1)P_{n+1}(x) - (2n + 1)xP_n(x) + nP_{n-1}(x) = 0, \qquad (7)$$

which is easily obtained, and is convenient when the numerical value of x is given.

Differentiate (5) with respect to z, and we get

$$\frac{-(z - x)}{(1 - 2xz + z^2)^{\frac{3}{2}}} = P_1(x) + 2P_2(x) \cdot z + 3P_3(x) \cdot z^2 + \ldots,$$

whence

$$\frac{-(z - x)}{(1 - 2xz + z^2)^{\frac{1}{2}}} = (1 - 2xz + z^2)(P_1(x) + 2P_2(x) \cdot z + 3P_3(x) \cdot z^2 + \ldots),$$

or by (5)

$$(1 - 2xz + z^2)(P_1(x) + 2P_2(x) \cdot z + 3P_3(x) \cdot z^2 \cdots)$$
$$+ (z - x)(P_0(x) + P_1(x) \cdot z + P_2(x) \cdot z^2 + \cdots) = 0. \quad (8)$$

Now (8) is identically true, hence the coefficient of each power of z must vanish. Picking out the coefficient of z^n and writing it equal to zero, we have formula (7) above.

By the aid of (7) a table of Zonal Harmonics is easily computed since we have $P_0(x) = 1$, and $P_1(x) = x$. Such a table for $x = \cos \theta$ is given at the end of this chapter.

ART. 13. PROBLEMS IN ZONAL HARMONICS.

In any problem on Potential if V is independent of ϕ so that we can use the form of Laplace's Equation employed in Art. 4, and if the value of V on the axis of X is known, and can be expressed as $\Sigma a_m r^m$ or as $\sum \dfrac{b_m}{r^{m+1}}$, we can write out our required solution as

$$V = \Sigma a_m r^m P_m(\cos \theta) \quad \text{or} \quad V = \sum \frac{b_m P_m(\cos \theta)}{r^{m+1}};$$

for since $P_m(1) = 1$ each of these forms reduces to the proper value on the axis; and as we have seen in Art. 4 each of them satisfies the reduced form of Laplace's Equation.

As an example, let us suppose a statical charge of M units of electricity placed on a conductor in the form of a thin circular disk, and let it be required to find the value of the Potential Function at any point in the "field of force" due to the charge.

The surface density at a point of the plate at a distance r from its centre is

$$\sigma = \frac{M}{4a\pi \sqrt{a^2 - r^2}}$$

and all points of the conductor are at potential $\dfrac{\pi M}{2a}$. See Pierce's Newtonian Potential Function (§ 61).

The value of the potential function at a point in the axis of the plate at the distance x from the plate can be obtained without difficulty by a simple integration, and proves to be

$$V = \frac{M}{2a} \cos^{-1} \frac{x^2 - a^2}{x^2 + a^2}. \tag{1}$$

The second member of (1) is easily developed into a power series.

$$\frac{M}{2a} \cos^{-1} \frac{x^2 - a^2}{x^2 + a^2}$$

$$= \frac{M}{a}\left[\frac{\pi}{2} - \frac{x}{a} + \frac{x^3}{3a^3} - \frac{x^5}{5a^5} + \frac{x^7}{7a^7} - \ldots\right] \text{ if } x < a \quad (2)$$

$$= \frac{M}{a}\left[\frac{a}{x} - \frac{a^3}{3x^3} + \frac{a^5}{5x^5} - \frac{a^7}{7x^7} + \ldots\right] \text{ if } x > a. \quad (3)$$

Hence

$$V = \frac{M}{a}\left[\frac{\pi}{2} - \frac{r}{a}P_1(\cos\theta) + \frac{1}{3}\frac{r^3}{a^3}P_3(\cos\theta)\right.$$

$$\left. - \frac{1}{5}\frac{r^5}{a^5}P_5(\cos\theta) + \ldots\right] \quad (4)$$

is our required solution if $r < a$ and $\theta < \dfrac{\pi}{2}$, as is

$$V = \frac{M}{a}\left[\frac{a}{r} - \frac{1}{3}\frac{a^3}{r^3}P_2(\cos\theta) + \frac{1}{5}\frac{a^5}{r^5}P_4(\cos\theta)\right.$$

$$\left. - \frac{1}{7}\frac{a^7}{r^7}P_6(\cos\theta) + \ldots\right] \text{ if } r > a. \quad (5)$$

The series in (4) and (5) are convergent, since they may be obtained from the convergent series (2) and (3) by multiplying the terms by a set of quantities no one of which exceeds one in absolute value. For it will be shown in the next article that $P_m(\cos\theta)$ always lies between 1 and -1.

Prob. 19. Find the value of the Potential Function due to the attraction of a material circular ring of small cross-section.

The value on the axis of the ring can be obtained by a simple integration, and is $\dfrac{M}{\sqrt{c^2 + r^2}}$ if M is the mass and c the radius of the ring. At any point in space, if $r < c$

$$V = \frac{M}{c}\left[P_0(\cos\theta) - \frac{1}{2}\frac{r^2}{c^2}P_2(\cos\theta) + \frac{1\cdot 3}{2\cdot 4}\frac{r^4}{c^4}P_4(\cos\theta) - \ldots\right],$$

and if $r > c$

$$V = \frac{M}{c} \left[\frac{c}{r} P_0(\cos \theta) - \frac{1}{2} \frac{c^3}{r^3} P_2(\cos \theta) + \frac{1 \cdot 3}{2 \cdot 4} \frac{c^5}{r^5} P_4(\cos \theta) - \ldots \right].$$

ART. 14. ADDITIONAL FORMS.

(a) We have seen in Art. 12 that $P_m(x)$ is the coefficient of z^m in the development of $(1 - 2xz + z^2)^{-\frac{1}{2}}$ in a power series.

$$(1 - 2xz + z^2)^{-\frac{1}{2}} = [1 - z(e^{\theta i} + e^{-\theta i}) + z^2]^{-\frac{1}{2}}$$
$$= (1 - ze^{\theta i})^{-\frac{1}{2}}(1 - ze^{-\theta i})^{-\frac{1}{2}}.$$

If we develop $(1 - ze^{\theta i})^{-\frac{1}{2}}$ and $(1 - ze^{-\theta i})^{-\frac{1}{2}}$ by the Binomial Theorem their product will give a development for $(1 - 2xz + z^2)^{-\frac{1}{2}}$. The coefficient of z^m is easily picked out and reduced, and we get

$$P_m(\cos \theta) =$$
$$\frac{1 \cdot 3 \cdot 5 \ldots (2m - 1)}{2 \cdot 4 \cdot 6 \ldots 2m} \left[2 \cos m\theta + 2 \frac{1 \cdot m}{1 \cdot (2m - 1)} \cos (m - 2)\theta \right.$$
$$\left. + 2 \frac{1 \cdot 3 \cdot m(m - 1)}{1 \cdot 2 \cdot (2m - 1)(2m - 3)} \cos (m - 4)\theta + \ldots \right] \qquad (1)$$

If m is odd the parenthesis in (1) ends with the term containing $\cos \theta$; if m is even, with the term containing $\cos 0$, but in the latter case the term in question will not be multiplied by the factor 2, which is common to all the other terms.

Since all the coefficients in the second member of (1) are positive, $P_m(\cos \theta)$ has its maximum value when $\theta = 0$, and its value then has already been shown in Art. 12 to be unity. Obviously, then, its minimum value cannot be less than $- 1$.

(b) If we integrate the value of $P_m(x)$ given in (11), Art. 4, m times in succession with respect to x, the result will be found to differ from $\frac{1 \cdot 3 \cdot 5 \ldots (2m - 1)}{(2m)!}(x^2 - 1)^m$ by terms involving lower powers of x than the mth.

Hence $\qquad P_m(x) = \frac{1}{2^m m!} \frac{d^m}{dx^m}(x^2 - 1)^m.$ $\qquad (2)$

(c) Other forms for $P_m(x)$, which we give without demonstration, are

$$P_m(x) = \frac{(-1)^m}{m!} \frac{\partial^m}{\partial x^m} \frac{1}{\sqrt{x^2+y^2+z^2}}. \tag{3}$$

$$P_m(x) = \frac{1}{\pi} \int_0^\pi [x + \sqrt{x^2-1} \cdot \cos \phi]^m d\phi. \tag{4}$$

$$P_m(x) = \frac{1}{\pi} \int_0^\pi \frac{d\phi}{[x - \sqrt{x^2-1} \cdot \cos \phi]^{m+1}}. \tag{5}$$

(4) and (5) can be verified without difficulty by expanding and integrating.

ART. 15. DEVELOPMENT IN TERMS OF ZONAL HARMONICS.

Whenever, as in Art. 4, we have the value of the Potential Function given on the surface of a sphere, and this value depends only on the distance from the extremity of a diameter, it becomes necessary to develop a function of θ into a series of the form

$$A_0 P_0(\cos \theta) + A_1 P_1(\cos \theta) + A_2 P_2(\cos \theta) + \ldots;$$

or, what amounts to the same thing, to develop a function of x into a series of the form

$$A_0 P_0(x) + A_1 P_1(x) + A_2 P_2(x) + \ldots.$$

The problem is entirely analogous to that of development in sine-series treated at length in Art. 6, and may be solved by the same method.

Assume $f(x) = A_0 P_0(x) + A_1 P_1(x) + A_2 P_2(x) + \ldots$ $\qquad$ (1)

for $-1 < x < 1$. Multiply (1) by $P_m(x)dx$ and integrate from -1 to 1. We get

$$\int_{-1}^1 f(x)P_m(x)dx = \sum_{n=0}^{n=\infty} [A_n \int_{-1}^1 P_m(x)P_n(x)dx]. \tag{2}$$

We shall show in the next article that

$$\int_{-1}^{1} P_m(x)P_n(x)dx = 0, \quad \text{unless } m = n,$$

and that

$$\int_{-1}^{1} [P_m(x)]^2 dx = \frac{2}{2m+1}.$$

Hence

$$A_m = \frac{2m+1}{2} \int_{-1}^{1} f(x)P_m(x)dx. \tag{3}$$

It is important to notice here, as in Art. 6, that the method we have used in obtaining A_m amounts essentially to determining A_m, so that the equation

$$f(x) = A_0 P_0(x) + A_1 P_1(x) + A_2 P_2(x) + \ldots + A_n P_n(x)$$

shall hold good for $n+1$ equidistant values of x between -1 and 1, and taking its limiting value as n is indefinitely increased.

ART. 16. FORMULAS FOR DEVELOPMENT.

We have seen in Art. 4 that $z = P_m(x)$ is a solution of Legendre's Equation $\dfrac{d}{dx}\left[(1 - x^2)\dfrac{dz}{dx}\right] + m(m+1)z = 0.$ (1)

Hence $\dfrac{d}{dx}\left[(1 - x^2)\dfrac{dP_m(x)}{dx}\right] + m(m+1)P_m(x) = 0,$ (2)

and $\dfrac{d}{dx}\left[(1 - x^2)\dfrac{dP_n(x)}{dx}\right] + n(n+1)P_n(x) = 0.$ (3)

Multiply (2) by $P_n(x)$ and (3) by $P_m(x)$, subtract, transpose, and integrate. We have

$$[m(m+1) - n(n+1)]\int_{-1}^{1} P_m(x)P_n(x)dx$$

$$= \int_{-1}^{1} P_m(x)\frac{d}{dx}\left[(1 - x^2)\frac{dP_n(x)}{dx}\right]dx$$

$$-\int_{-1}^{1} P_n(x)\frac{d}{dx}\left[(1-x^2)\frac{dP_m(x)}{dx}\right]dx \quad (4)$$

$$= \left[P_m(x)(1-x^2)\frac{dP_n(x)}{dx} - P_n(x)(1-x^2)\frac{dP_m(x)}{dx} \right]_{-1}^{1}$$

$$-\int_{-1}^{1}(1-x^2)\frac{dP_n(x)}{dx}\frac{dP_m(x)}{dx}\cdot dx$$

$$+\int_{-1}^{1}(1-x^2)\frac{dP_m(x)}{dx}\frac{dP_n(x)}{dx}\cdot dx \quad (5)$$

by integration by parts,

$$= 0.$$

Hence $$\int_{-1}^{1}P_m(x)P_n(x)dx = 0, \qquad (6)$$

unless $m = n$.

If in (4) we integrate from x to 1 instead of from -1 to 1, we get an important formula.

$$\int_{x}^{1}P_m(x)P_n(x)dx = \frac{(1-x^2)\left[P_n(x)\dfrac{dP_m(x)}{dx} - P_m(x)\dfrac{dP_n(x)}{dx} \right]}{m(m+1)-n(n+1)}, \quad (7)$$

and as a special case, since $P_0(x) = 1$.

$$\int_{x}^{1}P_m(x)dx = \frac{(1-x^2)\dfrac{dP_m(x)}{dx}}{m(m+1)}, \qquad (8)$$

unless $m = 0$.

To get $\int_{-1}^{1}[P_m(x)]^2dx$ is not particularly difficult. By (2), Art. 14,

$$\int_{-1}^{1}[P_m(x)]^2dx = \frac{1}{2^{2m}(m!)^2}\int_{-1}^{1}\frac{d^m(x^2-1)^m}{dx^m}\cdot\frac{d^m(x^2-1)^m}{dx^m}\cdot dx \quad (9)$$

By successive integrations by parts, noting that $\frac{d^{m-\kappa}}{dx^{m-\kappa}}(x^2-1)^m$ contains $(x^2-1)^\kappa$ as a factor if $\kappa < m$, and that $\dfrac{d^{2m}(x^2-1)^m}{dx^{2m}} = (2m)!$ we get

$$\int_{-1}^{1}[P_m(x)]^2dx = \frac{(-1)^m(2m)!}{2^{2m}(m!)^2}\int_{-1}^{1}(x^2-1)^mdx. \qquad (10)$$

$$\int_{-1}^{1}(x^2-1)^mdx = \int_{-1}^{1}(x-1)^m(x+1)^mdx$$

$$= -\frac{m}{m+1}\int_{-1}^{1}(x-1)^{m-1}(x+1)^{m+1}dx$$

$$= (-1)^m\frac{m!\,m!}{(2m)!}\int_{-1}^{1}(x+1)^{2m}dx = (-1)^m\frac{2^{2m+1}(m!)^2}{(2m+1)!}.$$

Hence $$\int_{-1}^{1}[P_m(x)]^2dx = \frac{2}{2m+1}. \qquad (11)$$

Prob. 20. Show that $\int_{0}^{1}P_m(x)dx = 0$ if m is even and is not zero

$$= (-1)^{\frac{m-1}{2}}\frac{1}{m(m+1)}\cdot\frac{3\cdot5\cdot7\cdots m}{2\cdot4\cdot6\cdots(m-1)} \text{ if } m \text{ is odd.}$$

Prob. 21. Show that $\int_{0}^{1}[P_m(x)]^2dx = \dfrac{1}{2m+1}$. Note that $[P_m(x)]^2$ is an even function of x.

Prob. 22. Show that if $f(x) = 0$ from $x = -1$ to $x = 0$, and $f(x) = 1$ from $x = 0$ to $x = 1$,

$$f(x) = \frac{1}{2}+\frac{3}{4}P_1(x)-\frac{7}{8}\cdot\frac{1}{2}P_3(x)+\frac{11}{12}\cdot\frac{1\cdot3}{2\cdot4}P_5(x)-\cdots$$

Prob. 23. Show that $F(\theta) = \overset{m=\infty}{\underset{m=0}{\Sigma}}B_mP_m(\cos\theta)$ where

$$B_m = \frac{2m+1}{2}\int_{0}^{\pi}F(\theta)P_m(\cos\theta)\sin\theta\,d\theta.$$

Prob. 24. Show that

$$\csc \theta = \frac{\pi}{2}\left[1 + 5\left(\frac{1}{2}\right)^2 P_2(\cos \theta) + 9\left(\frac{1\cdot 3}{2\cdot 4}\right)^2 P_4(\cos \theta) + \ldots\right].$$

See (1), Art. 14.

Prob. 25. Show that

$$x^n = \frac{n!}{1\cdot 3\cdot 5\cdots(2n+1)}\left[(2n+1)P_n(x) + (2n-3)\frac{2n+1}{2}P_{n-2}(x)\right.$$

$$\left. + (2n-7)\frac{(2n+1)(2n-1)}{2\cdot 4}P_{n-4}(x) + \ldots\right].$$

Note that $\displaystyle\int_{-1}^{1} x^n P_m(x)dx = \frac{1}{2^m m!}\int_{-1}^{1} x^n \frac{d^m(x^2-1)^m}{dx^m}dx$, and use the

method of integration by parts freely.

Prob. 26. Show that if V is the value of the Potential Function at any point in a field of force, not imbedded in attracting or repelling matter; and if $V = f(\theta)$ when $r = a$,

$$V = \Sigma A_m \frac{r^m}{a^m} P_m(\cos \theta) \text{ if } r < a$$

and $$V = \Sigma A_m \frac{a^{m+1}}{r^{m+1}} P_m(\cos \theta) \text{ if } r > a,$$

where $$A_m = \frac{2m+1}{2}\int_{0}^{\pi} f(\theta)P_m(\cos \theta) \sin \theta d\theta.$$

Prob. 27. Show that if

$$V = c \text{ when } r = a; \quad V = c \text{ if } r < a, \quad \text{and } V = \frac{ca}{r} \text{ if } r > a.$$

Art. 17. Formulas in Zonal Harmonics.

The following formulas which we give without demonstration may be found useful for reference:

$$\frac{dP_n(x)}{dx} = (2n-1)P_{n-1}(x) + (2n-5)P_{n-3}(x) + (2n-9)P_{n-5}(x) + \ldots (1)$$

$$\frac{dP_{n+1}(x)}{dx} - \frac{dP_{n-1}(x)}{dx} = (2n+1)P_n(x) \qquad (2)$$

$$\int_{x}^{1} P_n(x)dx = \frac{1}{2n+1}[P_{n-1}(x) - P_{n+1}(x)]. \qquad (3)$$

ART. 18. SPHERICAL HARMONICS.

In problems in Potential where the value of V is given on the surface of a sphere, but is not independent of the angle ϕ, we have to solve Laplace's Equation in the form (5), Art. 1, and by a treatment analogous to that given in Art. 4 it can be proved that

$$V = r^m \cos n\phi \, \sin^n \theta \frac{d^n P_m(\mu)}{d\mu_n} \quad \text{and} \quad V = r^m \sin n\phi \, \sin^n \theta \frac{d^n P_m(\mu)}{d\mu^n},$$

where $\mu = \cos \theta$, are particular solutions of (5), Art. 1.

The factors multiplied by r^m in these values are known as Tesseral Harmonics. They are functions of ϕ and θ, and they play nearly the same part in unsymmetrical problems that the Zonal Harmonics play in those independent of ϕ.

$$Y_m(\mu, \, \phi) = A_0 P_m(\mu) + \sum_{m=1}^{n=m} (A_n \cos n\phi + B_n \sin n\phi) \sin^n \theta \frac{d^n P_m(\mu)}{d\mu^n}$$

is known as a Surface Spherical Harmonic of the mth degree,

and $$V = r^m Y_m(\mu, \, \phi) \quad \text{and} \quad V = \frac{1}{r^{m+1}} Y_m(\mu, \, \phi)$$

satisfy Laplace's Equation, (5), Art. 1.

The Tesseral and the Zonal Harmonics are special cases of the Spherical Harmonic, as is also a form $P_m(\cos \gamma)$ known as a Laplace's Coefficient or a Laplacian; γ standing for the angle between r and the radius vector r_1 of some fixed point.

For the properties and uses of Spherical Harmonics we refer the student to more extended treatises, namely, to Ferrer's Spherical Harmonics, to Heine's Kugelfunctionen, or to Byerly's Fourier's Series and Spherical Harmonics.

ART. 19.* BESSEL'S FUNCTIONS. PROPERTIES.

We have seen in Art. 5 that $z = J_0(x)$ where

$$J_0(x) = 1 - \frac{x^2}{2^2} + \frac{x^4}{2^2 \cdot 4^2} - \frac{x^6}{2^2 \cdot 4^2 \cdot 6^2} + \cdots \quad (1)$$

* The student should review Art. 5 before reading this article.

is a solution of the equation

$$\frac{d^2z}{dx^2} + \frac{1}{x}\frac{dz}{dx} + z = 0; \qquad (2)$$

and we have called $J_0(x)$ a Bessel's Function or Cylindrical Harmonic of the zero order.

$$J_1(x) = -\frac{dJ_0(x)}{dx} = \frac{x}{2}\left[1 - \frac{x^2}{2 \cdot 4} + \frac{x^4}{2 \cdot 4^2 \cdot 6} - \frac{x^6}{2 \cdot 4^2 \cdot 6^2 \cdot 8} + \cdots\right] (3)$$

is called a Bessel's Function of the first order, and

$$z' = J_1(x)$$

is a solution of the equation

$$\frac{d^2z'}{dx^2} + \frac{1}{x}\frac{dz'}{dx} + \left(1 - \frac{1}{x^2}\right)z' = 0, \qquad (4)$$

which is the result of differentiating (2) with respect to x.

A table giving values of $J_0(x)$ and $J_1(x)$ will be found at the end of this chapter.

If we write $J_0(x)$ for z in equation (2), then multiply through by xdx and integrate from zero to x, simplifying the resulting equation by integration by parts, we get

$$\frac{xdJ_0(x)}{dx} + \int_0^x xJ_0(x)dx = 0,$$

or, since $J_1(x) = -\dfrac{dJ_0(x)}{dx}$,

$$\int_0^x xJ_0(x)dx = xJ_1(x). \qquad (5)$$

If we write $J_0(x)$ for z in equation (2), then multiply through by $x^2\dfrac{dJ_0(x)}{dx}$, and integrate from zero to x, simplifying by integration by parts, we get

$$\frac{x^2}{2}\left[\left(\frac{dJ_0(x)}{dx}\right)^2 + (J_0(x))^2\right] - \int_0^x x(J_0(x))^2dx = 0,$$

or

$$\int_0^x x(J_0(x))^2dx = \frac{x^2}{2}\left[(J_0(x))^2 + (J_1(x))^2\right]. \qquad (6)$$

If we replace x by μx in (2) it becomes

$$\frac{d^2z}{dx^2} + \frac{1}{x}\frac{dz}{dx} + \mu^2 z = 0 \tag{7}$$

(See (8), Art. 5). Hence $z = J_0(\mu x)$ is a solution of (7).

If we substitute in turn in (7) $J_0(\mu_\kappa x)$ and $J_0(\mu_\iota x)$ for z, multiply the first equation by $x J_0(\mu_\iota x)$, the second by $x J_0(\mu_\kappa x)$, subtract the second from the first, simplify by integration by parts, and reduce, we get

$$\int_0^a x J_0(\mu_\kappa x) J_0(\mu_\iota x) dx$$

$$= \frac{1}{\mu_\kappa^2 - \mu_\iota^2}[\mu_\kappa a J_0(\mu_\iota a) J_1(\mu_\kappa a) - \mu_\iota a J_0(\mu_\kappa a) J_1(\mu_\iota a)]. \tag{8}$$

Hence if μ_κ and μ_ι are different roots of $J_0(\mu a) = 0$, or of $J_1(\mu a) = 0$, or of $\mu a J_1(\mu a) - \lambda J_0(\mu a) = 0$,

$$\int_0^a x J_0(\mu_\kappa x) J_0(\mu_\iota x) dx = 0. \tag{9}$$

We give without demonstration the following formulas, which are sometimes useful:

$$J_0(x) = \frac{1}{\pi}\int_0^\pi \cos(x \cos \phi) d\phi. \tag{10}$$

$$J_1(x) = \frac{x}{\pi}\int_0^\pi \sin^2 \phi \cos(x \cos \phi) d\phi. \tag{11}$$

They can be confirmed by developing $\cos(x \cos \phi)$, integrating, and comparing with (1) and (3).

Art. 20. Applications of Bessel's Functions.

(a) The problem of Art. 5 is a special case of the following: The convex surface and one base of a cylinder of radius a and length b are kept at the constant temperature zero, the temperature at each point of the other base is a given function of the distance of the point from the center of the base; required the temperature of any point of the cylinder after the permanent temperatures have been established.

Here we have to solve Laplace's Equation in the form

$$\frac{\partial^2 u}{\partial r^2} + \frac{1}{r}\frac{\partial u}{\partial r} + \frac{\partial^2 u}{\partial z^2} = 0 \tag{1}$$

(see Art. 5), subject to the conditions

$$u = 0 \text{ when } z = 0,$$
$$u = 0 \quad \text{``} \quad r = a,$$
$$u = f(r) \text{ ``} \quad z = b.$$

Starting with the particular solution of (1),

$$u = \sinh (\mu z) J_0(\mu r), \tag{2}$$

and proceeding as in Art. 5, we get, if $\mu_1, \mu_2, \mu_3, \ldots$ are roots of

$$J_0(\mu a) = 0, \tag{3}$$

and

$$f(r) = A_1 J_0(\mu_1 r) + A_2 J_0(\mu_2 r) + A_3 J_0(\mu_3 r) + \ldots, \tag{4}$$

$$u = A_1\frac{\sinh (\mu_1 z)}{\sinh (\mu_1 b)} J_0(\mu_1 r) + A_2\frac{\sinh (\mu_2 z)}{\sinh (\mu_2 b)} J_0(\mu_2 r) + \ldots. \tag{5}$$

(*b*) If instead of keeping the convex surface of the cylinder at temperature zero we surround it by a jacket impervious to heat the equation of condition, $u = 0$ when $r = a$, will be replaced by $\dfrac{\partial u}{\partial r} = 0$ when $r = a$, or if $u = \sinh (\mu z) J_0(\mu r)$ by

$$\frac{d J_0(\mu r)}{dr} = 0 \quad \text{when } r = a,$$

that is, by $-\mu J_1(\mu a) = 0$

or $J_1(\mu a) = 0. \tag{6}$

If now in (4) and (5) $\mu_1, \mu_2, \mu_3, \ldots$ are roots of (6), (5) will be the solution of our new problem.

(*c*) If instead of keeping the convex surface of the cylinder at the temperature zero we allow it to cool in air which is at the temperature zero, the condition $u = 0$ when $r = a$ will be replaced by $\dfrac{\partial u}{\partial r} + hu = 0$ when $r = a$, h being the coefficient of surface conductivity.

If $u = \sinh{(\mu z)}J_0(\mu r)$ this condition becomes

$$- \mu J_1(\mu r) + h J_0(\mu r) = 0 \quad \text{when} \quad r = a,$$

or $$\mu a J_1(\mu a) - a h J_0(\mu a) = 0. \tag{7}$$

If now in (4) and (5) μ_1, μ_2, μ_3, ... are roots of (7), (5) will be the solution of our present problem.

It can be shown that

$$J_0(x) = 0, \tag{8}$$

$$J_1(x) = 0, \tag{9}$$

and $$x J_1(x) - \lambda J_0(x) = 0 \tag{10}$$

have each an infinite number of real positive roots.* The earlier roots of these equations can be obtained without serious difficulty from the table for $J_0(x)$ and $J_1(x)$ at the end of this chapter.

ART. 21. DEVELOPMENT IN TERMS OF BESSEL'S FUNCTIONS.

We shall now obtain the developments called for in the last article.

Let $$f(r) = A_1 J_0(\mu_1 r) + A_2 J_0(\mu_2 r) + A_3 J_0(\mu_3 r) + \cdots \tag{1}$$

μ_1, μ_2, μ_3, etc., being roots of $J_0(\mu a) = 0$, or of $J_1(\mu a) = 0$, or

of $$\mu a J_1(\mu a) - \lambda J_0(\mu a) = 0.$$

To determine any coefficient A_k multiply (1) by $r J_0(\mu_k r) dr$ and integrate from zero to a. The first member will become

$$\int_0^a r f(r) J_0(\mu_k r) dr.$$

Every term of the second member will vanish by (9), Art. 19, except the term

$$A_k \int_0^a r \, [J_0(\mu_k r)]^2 dr.$$

$$\int_0^a r [J_0(\mu_k r)]^2 dr = \frac{1}{\mu_k^2} \int_0^{\mu_k a} x [J_0(x)]^2 dx = \frac{a^2}{2} \left([J_0(\mu_k a)]^2 + [J_1(\mu_k a)]^2 \right)$$

by (6), Art. 19.

* See Riemann's Partielle Differentialgleichungen, § 97.

Hence $A_k = \dfrac{2}{a^2\left([J_0(\mu_k a)]^2 + [J_1(\mu_k a)]^2\right)} \displaystyle\int_0^a rf(r)J_0(\mu_k r)dr.$ (2)

The development (1) holds good from $r = 0$ to $r = a$ (see Arts. 6 and 15).

If μ_1, μ_2, μ_3, etc., are roots of $J_0(\mu a) = 0$, (2) reduces to

$$A_k = \frac{2}{a^2[J_1(\mu_k a)]^2}\int_0^a rf(r)J_0(\mu_k r)dr. \tag{3}$$

If μ_1, μ_2, μ_3, etc., are roots of $J_1(\mu a) = 0$, (2) reduces to

$$A_k = \frac{2}{a^2[J_0(\mu_k a)]^2}\int_0^a rf(r)J_0(\mu_k r)dr. \tag{4}$$

If μ_1, μ_2, μ_3, etc., are roots of $\mu a J_1(\mu a) - \lambda J_0(\mu a) = 0$, (2) reduces to

$$A_k = \frac{2\mu_k^2}{(\lambda^2 + \mu_k^2 a^2)[J_0(\mu_k a)]^2}\int_0^a rf(r)J_0(\mu_k r)dr. \tag{5}$$

For the important case where $f(r) = 1$

$$\int_0^a rf(r)J_0(\mu_k r)dr = \int_0^a rJ_0(\mu_k r)dr = \frac{1}{\mu_k^2}\int_0^{\mu_k a} xJ_0(x)dx = \frac{a}{\mu_k}J_1(\mu_k a) \tag{6}$$

by (5), Art. 19; and (3) reduces to

$$A_k = \frac{2}{\mu_k a J_1(\mu_k a)}; \tag{7}$$

(4) reduces to

$$A_k = 0, \tag{8}$$

except for $k = 1$, when $\mu_k = 0$, and we have

$$A_1 = 1; \tag{9}$$

(5) reduces to $\qquad A_k = \dfrac{2\lambda}{(\lambda^2 + \mu_k^2 a^2)J_0(\mu_k a)}.$ (10)

Prob. 28. A cylinder of radius one meter and altitude one meter has its upper surface kept at the temperature 100°, and its base and convex surface at the temperature 15°, until the stationary temperatures are established. Find the temperature at points on the axis 25, 50, and 75 centimeters from the base, and also at a point 25 centimeters from the base and 50 centimeters from the axis.

Ans. 29°.6; 47°.6; 71°.2; 25°.8

Prob. 29. An iron cylinder one meter long and 20 centimeters in diameter has its convex surface covered with a so-called non-conducting cement one centimeter thick. One end and the convex surface of the cylinder thus coated are kept at the temperature zero, the other end at the temperature of 100 degrees. Given that the conductivity of iron is 0.185 and of cement 0.000162 in C. G. S. units.

Find to the nearest tenth of a degree the temperature of the middle point of the axis, and of the points of the axis 20 centimeters from each end after the temperatures have ceased to change.

Find also the temperature of a point on the surface midway between the ends, and of points of the surface 20 centimeters from each end. Find the temperatures of the three points of the axis, supposing the coating a perfect non-conductor, and again, supposing the coating absent. Neglect the curvature of the coating. Ans. $15°.4$; $40°.85$; $72°.8$; $15°.3$; $40°.7$; $72°.5$; $0°.0$; $0°.0$; $1°.3$.

Prob. 30. If the temperature at any point in an infinitely long cylinder of radius c is initially a function of the distance of the point from the axis, the temperature at any time must satisfy the equation $\dfrac{\partial u}{\partial t} = a^2 \left(\dfrac{\partial^2 u}{\partial r^2} + \dfrac{1}{r} \dfrac{\partial u}{\partial r} \right)$ (see Art. 1), since it is clearly independent of z and ϕ.

Show that

$$u = A_1 e^{-a^2 \mu_1^2 t} J_0(\mu_1 r) + A_2 e^{-a^2 \mu_2^2 t} J_0(\mu_2 r) \\ + A_3 e^{-a^2 \mu_3^2 t} J_0(\mu_3 r) + \cdots,$$

where, if the surface of the cylinder is kept at the temperature zero, $\mu_1, \mu_2, \mu_3, \ldots$ are roots of $J_0(\mu c) = 0$ and A_k is the value given in (3) with c written in place of a ; if the surface of the cylinder is adiabatic $\mu_1, \mu_2, \mu_3, \ldots$ are roots of $J_1(\mu c) = 0$ and A_k is obtained from (4); and if heat escapes at the surface into air at the temperature zero $\mu_1, \mu_2, \mu_3, \ldots$ are roots of $\mu c J_1(\mu c) - \lambda J_0(\mu c) = 0$, and A_k is obtained from (5).

Prob. 31. If the cylinder described in problem 29 is very long and is initially at the temperature $100°$ throughout, and the convex surface is kept at the temperature $0°$, find the temperature of a point 5 centimeters from the axis 15 minutes after cooling has begun ; first when the cylinder is coated, and second, when the coating is absent. Ans. $97°.2$; $0°.01$.

Prob. 32. A circular drumhead of radius a is initially slightly distorted into a given form which is a surface of revolution about the axis of the drum, and is then allowed to vibrate, and z is the ordinate of any point of the membrane at any time. Assuming that

z must satisfy the equation $\dfrac{\partial^2 z}{\partial t^2} = c^2 \left(\dfrac{\partial^2 z}{\partial r^2} + \dfrac{1}{r} \dfrac{\partial z}{\partial r} \right)$, subject to the conditions $z = 0$ when $r = a$, $\dfrac{\partial z}{\partial t} = 0$ when $t = 0$, and $z = f(r)$ when $t = 0$, show that $z = A_1 J_0(\mu_1 r) \cos \mu_1 ct + A_2 J_0(\mu_2 r) \cos \mu_2 ct + \ldots$ where $\mu_1, \mu_2, \mu_3, \ldots$ are roots of $J_0(\mu a) = 0$ and A_k has the value given in (3).

Prob. 33. Show that if a drumhead be initially distorted as in problem 32 it will not in general give a musical note ; that it may be initially distorted so as to give a musical note ; that in this case the vibration will be a steady vibration ; that the periods of the various musical notes that can be given are proportional to the roots of $J_0(x) = 0$, and that the possible nodal lines for such vibrations are concentric circles whose radii are proportional to the roots of $J_0(x) = 0$.

ART. 22. PROBLEMS IN BESSEL'S FUNCTIONS.

If in a problem on the stationary temperatures of a cylinder $u = 0$ when $z = 0$, $u = 0$ when $z = b$, and $u = f(z)$ when $r = a$, the problem is easily solved. If in (2), Art. 20, and in the corresponding solution $z = \cosh(\mu z) J_0(\mu r)$ we replace μ by μi, we can readily obtain $z = \sin(\mu z) J_0(\mu r i)$ and $z = \cos(\mu z) J_0(\mu r i)$ as particular solutions of (1), Art. 20 ; and

$$J_0(xi) = 1 + \frac{x^2}{2} + \frac{x^4}{2^2 . 4^2} + \frac{x^6}{2^2 . 4^2 . 6^2} + \ldots \qquad (1)$$

and is real.

$$f(z) = \sum_{k=1}^{k=\infty} A_k \sin \frac{k\pi z}{b}$$

where

$$A_k = \frac{2}{b} \int_0^b f(z) \sin \frac{k\pi z}{b} \, dz \qquad (2)$$

by Art. 9.

Hence

$$u = \sum_{k=1}^{k=\infty} A_k \sin \frac{k\pi z}{b} \frac{J_0 \left(\dfrac{k\pi r i}{b} \right)}{J_0 \left(\dfrac{k\pi a i}{b} \right)} \qquad (3)$$

is the required solution.

A table giving the values of $J_0(xi)$ will be found at the end of this chapter.

Prob. 34. A cylinder two feet long and two feet in diameter has its bases kept at the temperature zero and its convex surface at 100 degrees Centigrade until the internal temperatures have ceased to change. Find the temperature of a point on the axis half way between the bases, and of a point six inches from the axis, half way between the bases. Ans. $72.^{\circ}1$; $80^{\circ}.1$.

ART. 23. BESSEL'S FUNCTIONS OF HIGHER ORDER.

If we are dealing with Laplace's Equation in Cylindrical Coordinates and the problem is not symmetrical about an axis, functions of the form

$$J_n(x) = \frac{x^n}{2^n \Gamma(n+1)}\left[1 - \frac{x^2}{2^2(n+1)} + \frac{x^4}{2^4 \cdot 2!(n+1)(n+2)} - \cdots \right]$$

play very much the same part as that played by $J_0(x)$ in the preceding articles. They are known as Bessel's Functions of the nth order. In problems concerning hollow cylinders much more complicated functions enter, known as Bessel's Functions of the second kind.

For a very brief discussion of these functions the reader is referred to Byerly's Fourier's Series and Spherical Harmonics; for a much more complete treatment to Gray and Matthews' admirable treatise on Bessel's Functions.

ART. 24. LAMÉ'S FUNCTIONS.

Complicated problems in Potential and in allied subjects are usually handled by the aid of various forms of curvilinear co-ördinates, and each form has its appropriate Harmonic Functions, which are usually extremely complicated. For instance, Lamé's Functions or Ellipsoidal Harmonics are used when solutions of Laplace's Equation in Ellipsoidal coordinates are required; Toroidal Harmonics when solutions of Laplace's Equation in Toroidal coordinates are needed.

For a brief introduction to the theory of these functions see Byerly's Fourier's Series and Spherical Harmonics.

HARMONIC FUNCTIONS.

TABLE I. SURFACE ZONAL HARMONICS.

θ	$P_1 (\cos \theta)$	$P_2 (\cos \theta)$	$P_3 (\cos \theta)$	$P_4 (\cos \theta)$	$P_5 (\cos \theta)$	$P_6 (\cos \theta)$	$P_7 (\cos \theta)$
0°	1.0000	1.0000	1.0000	1.0000	1.0000	1.0000	1.0000
1	.9998	.9995	.9991	.9985	.9977	.9967	.9955
2	.9994	.9982	.9963	.9939	.9909	.9872	.9829
3	.9986	.9959	.9918	.9863	.9795	.9713	.9617
4	.9976	.9927	.9854	.9758	.9638	.9495	.9329
5	.9962	.9886	.9773	.9623	.9437	.9216	.8961
6	.9945	.9836	.9674	.9459	.9194	.8881	.8522
7	.9925	.9777	.9557	.9267	.8911	.8476	.7986
8	.9903	.9709	.9423	.9048	.8589	.8053	.7448
9	.9877	.9633	.9273	.8803	.8232	.7571	.6831
10	.9848	.9548	.9106	.8532	.7840	.7045	.6164
11	.9816	.9454	.8923	.8238	.7417	.6483	.5461
12	.9781	.9352	.8724	.7920	.6966	.5892	.4732
13	.9744	.9241	.8511	.7582	.6489	.5273	.3940
14	.9703	.9122	.8283	.7224	.5990	.4635	.3219
15	.9659	.8995	.8042	.6847	.5471	.3982	.2454
16	.9613	.8860	.7787	.6454	.4937	.3322	.1699
17	.9563	.8718	.7519	.6046	.4391	.2660	.0961
18	.9511	.8568	.7240	.5624	.3836	.2002	.0289
19	.9455	.8410	.6950	.5192	.3276	.1347	−.0443
20	.9397	.8245	.6649	.4750	.2715	.0719	−.1072
21	.9336	.8074	.6338	.4300	.2156	.0107	−.1662
22	.9272	.7895	.6019	.3845	.1602	−.0481	−.2201
23	.9205	.7710	.5692	.3386	.1057	−.1038	−.2681
24	.9135	.7518	.5357	.2926	.0525	−.1559	−.3095
25	.9063	.7321	.5016	.2465	.0009	−.2053	−.3463
26	.8988	.7117	.4670	.2007	−.0489	−.2478	−.3717
27	.8910	.6908	.4319	.1553	−.0964	−.2869	−.3921
28	.8829	.6694	.3964	.1105	−.1415	−.3211	−.4052
29	.8746	.6474	.3607	.0665	−.1839	−.3503	−.4114
30	.8660	.6250	.3248	.0234	−.2233	−.3740	−.4101
31	.8572	.6021	.2887	−.0185	−.2595	−.3924	−.4022
32	.8480	.5788	.2527	−.0591	−.2923	−.4052	−.3876
33	.8387	.5551	.2167	−.0982	−.3216	−.4126	−.3670
34	.8290	.5310	.1809	−.1357	−.3473	−.4148	−.3409
35	.8192	.5065	.1454	−.1714	−.3691	−.4115	−.3096
36	.8090	.4818	.1102	−.2052	−.3871	−.4031	−.2738
37	.7986	.4567	.0755	−.2370	−.4011	−.3898	−.2343
38	.7880	.4314	.0413	−.2666	−.4112	−.3719	−.1918
39	.7771	.4059	.0077	−.2940	−.4174	−.3497	−.1469
40	.7660	.3802	−.0252	−.3190	−.4197	−.3234	−.1003
41	.7547	.3544	−.0574	−.3416	−.4181	−.2938	−.0534
42	.7431	.3284	−.0887	−.3616	−.4128	−.2611	−.0065
43	.7314	.3023	−.1191	−.3791	−.4038	−.2255	.0398
44	.7193	.2762	−.1485	−.3940	−.3914	−.1878	.0846
45°	.7071	.2500	−.1768	−.4062	−.3757	−.1485	.1270

TABLE I. SURFACE ZONAL HARMONICS.

θ	$P_1(\cos\theta)$	$P_2(\cos\theta)$	$P_3(\cos\theta)$	$P_4(\cos\theta)$	$P_5(\cos\theta)$	$P_6(\cos\theta)$	$P_7(\cos\theta)$
45°	.7071	.2500	−.1768	−.4062	−.3757	−.1485	.1270
46	.6947	.2238	−.2040	−.4158	−.3568	−.1079	.1666
47	.6820	.1977	−.2300	−.4252	−.3350	−.0645	.2054
48	.6691	.1716	−.2547	−.4270	−.3105	−.0251	.2349
49	.6561	.1456	−.2781	−.4286	−.2836	.0161	.2627
50	.6428	.1198	−.3002	−.4275	−.2545	.0563	.2854
51	.6293	.0941	−.3209	−.4239	−.2235	.0954	.3031
52	.6157	.0686	−.3401	−.4178	−.1910	.1326	.3153
53	.6018	.0433	−.3578	−.4093	−.1571	.1677	.3221
54	.5878	.0182	−.3740	−.3984	−.1223	.2002	.3234
55	.5736	−.0065	−.3886	−.3852	−.0868	.2297	.3191
56	.5592	−.0310	−.4016	−.3698	−.0510	.2559	.3095
57	.5446	−.0551	−.4131	−.3524	−.0150	.2787	.2949
58	.5299	−.0788	−.4229	−.3331	.0206	.2976	.2752
59	.5150	−.1021	−.4310	−.3119	.0557	.3125	.2511
60	.5000	−.1250	−.4375	−.2891	.0898	.3232	.2231
61	.4848	−.1474	−.4423	−.2647	.1229	.3298	.1916
62	.4695	−.1694	−.4455	−.2390	.1545	.3321	.1571
63	.4540	−.1908	−.4471	−.2121	.1844	.3302	.1203
64	.4384	−.2117	−.4470	−.1841	.2123	.3240	.0818
65	.4226	−.2321	−.4452	−.1552	.2381	.3138	.0422
66	.4067	−.2518	−.4419	−.1256	.2615	.2996	.0021
67	.3907	−.2710	−.4370	−.0955	.2824	.2819	−.0375
68	.3746	−.2896	−.4305	−.0650	.3005	.2605	−.0763
69	.3584	−.3074	−.4225	−.0344	.3158	.2361	−.1135
70	.3420	−.3245	−.4130	−.0038	.3281	.2089	−.1485
71	.3256	−.3410	−.4021	.0267	.3373	.1786	−.1811
72	.3090	−.3568	−.3898	.0568	.3434	.1472	−.2099
73	.2924	−.3718	−.3761	.0864	.3463	.1144	−.2347
74	.2756	−.3860	−.3611	.1153	.3461	.0795	−.2559
75	.2588	−.3995	−.3449	.1434	.3427	.0431	−.2730
76	.2419	−.4112	−.3275	.1705	.3362	.0076	−.2848
77	.2250	−.4241	−.3090	.1964	.3267	−.0284	−.2919
78	.2079	−.4352	−.2894	.2211	.3143	−.0644	−.2943
79	.1908	−.4454	−.2688	.2443	.2990	−.0989	−.2913
80	.1736	−.4548	−.2474	.2659	.2810	−.1321	−.2835
81	.1564	−.4633	−.2251	.2859	.2606	−.1635	−.2709
82	.1392	−.4709	−.2020	.3040	.2378	−.1926	−.2536
83	.1219	−.4777	−.1783	.3203	.2129	−.2193	−.2321
84	.1045	−.4836	−.1539	.3345	.1861	−.2431	−.2067
85	.0872	−.4886	−.1291	.3468	.1577	−.2638	−.1779
86	.0698	−.4927	−.1038	.3569	.1278	−.2811	−.1460
87	.0523	−.4959	−.0781	.3648	.0969	−.2947	−.1117
88	.0349	−.4982	−.0522	.3704	.0651	−.3045	−.0735
89	.0175	−.4995	−.0262	.3739	.0327	−.3105	−.0381
90°	.0000	−.5000	.0000	.3750	.0000	−.3125	.0000

HARMONIC FUNCTIONS.

TABLE II. BESSEL'S FUNCTIONS.

x	$J_0(x)$	$J_1(x)$	x	$J_0(x)$	$J_1(x)$	x	$J_0(x)$	$J_1(x)$
0.0	1.0000	0.0000	5.0	−.1776	−.3276	10.0	−.2459	.0435
0.1	.9975	.0499	5.1	−.1443	−.3371	10.1	−.2490	.0184
0.2	.9900	.0995	5.2	−.1103	−.3432	10.2	−.2496	.0066
0.3	.9776	.1483	5.3	−.0758	−.3460	10.3	−.2477	−.0313
0.4	.9604	.1960	5.4	−.0412	−.3453	10.4	−.2434	−.0555
0.5	.9385	.2423	5.5	−.0068	−.3414	10.5	−.2366	−.0789
0.6	.9120	.2867	5.6	.0270	−.3343	10.6	−.2276	−.1012
0.7	.8812	.3290	5.7	.0599	−.3241	10.7	−.2164	−.1224
0.8	.8463	.3688	5.8	.0917	−.3110	10.8	−.2032	−.1422
0.9	.8075	.4060	5.9	.1220	−.2951	10.9	−.1881	−.1604
1.0	.7652	.4401	6.0	.1506	−.2767	11.0	−.1712	−.1768
1.1	.7196	.4709	6.1	.1773	−.2559	11.1	−.1528	−.1913
1.2	.6711	.4983	6.2	.2017	−.2329	11.2	−.1330	−.2039
1.3	.6201	.5220	6.3	.2238	−.2081	11.3	−.1121	−.2143
1.4	.5669	.5419	6.4	.2433	−.1816	11.4	−.0902	−.2225
1.5	.5118	.5579	6.5	.2601	−.1538	11.5	−.0677	−.2284
1.6	.4554	.5699	6.6	.2740	−.1250	11.6	−.0446	−.2320
1.7	.3980	.5778	6.7	.2851	−.0953	11.7	−.0213	−.2333
1.8	.3400	.5815	6.8	.2931	−.0652	11.8	.0020	−.2323
1.9	.2818	.5812	6.9	.2981	−.0349	11.9	.0250	−.2290
2.0	.2239	.5767	7.0	.3001	−.0047	12.0	.0477	−.2234
2.1	.1666	.5683	7.1	.2991	.0252	12.1	.0697	−.2157
2.2	.1104	.5560	7.2	.2951	.0543	12.2	.0908	−.2060
2.3	.0555	.5399	7.3	.2882	.0826	12.3	.1108	−.1943
2.4	.0025	.5202	7.4	.2786	.1096	12.4	.1296	−.1807
2.5	−.0484	.4971	7.5	.2663	.1352	12.5	.1469	−.1655
2.6	−.0968	.4708	7.6	.2516	.1592	12.6	.1626	−.1487
2.7	−.1424	.4416	7.7	.2346	.1813	12.7	.1766	−.1307
2.8	−.1850	.4097	7.8	.2154	.2014	12.8	.1887	−.1114
2.9	−.2243	.3754	7.9	.1944	.2192	12.9	.1988	−.0912
3.0	−.2601	.3391	8.0	.1717	.2346	13.0	.2069	−.0703
3.1	−.2921	.3009	8.1	.1475	.2476	13.1	.2129	−.0489
3.2	−.3202	.2613	8.2	.1222	.2580	13.2	.2167	−.0271
3.3	−.3443	.2207	8.3	.0960	.2657	13.3	.2183	−.0052
3.4	−.3643	.1792	8.4	.0692	.2708	13.4	.2177	.0166
3.5	−.3801	.1374	8.5	.0419	.2731	13.5	.2150	.0380
3.6	−.3918	.0955	8.6	.0146	.2728	13.6	.2101	.0590
3.7	−.3992	.0538	8.7	−.0125	.2697	13.7	.2032	.0791
3.8	−.4026	.0128	8.8	−.0392	.2641	13.8	.1943	.0984
3.9	−.4018	−.0272	8.9	−.0653	.2559	13.9	.1836	.1166
4.0	−.3972	−.0660	9.0	−.0903	.2453	14.0	.1711	.1334
4.1	−.3887	−.1033	9.1	−.1142	.2324	14.1	.1570	.1488
4.2	−.3766	−.1386	9.2	−.1367	.2174	14.2	.1414	.1626
4.3	−.3610	−.1719	9.3	−.1577	.2004	14.3	.1245	.1747
4.4	−.3423	−.2028	9.4	−.1768	.1816	14.4	.1065	.1850
4.5	−.3205	−.2311	9.5	−.1939	.1613	14.5	.0875	.1934
4.6	−.2961	−.2566	9.6	−.2090	.1395	14.6	.0679	.1999
4.7	−.2693	−.2791	9.7	−.2218	.1166	14.7	.0476	.2043
4.8	−.2404	−.2985	9.8	−.2323	.0928	14.8	.0271	.2066
4.9	−.2097	−.3147	9.9	−.2403	.0684	14.9	.0064	.2069
5.0	−.1776	−.3276	10.0	−.2459	.0435	15.0	−.0142	.2051

TABLE III.—ROOTS OF BESSEL'S FUNCTIONS.

n	x_n for $J_0(x_n) = 0$	x_n for $J_1(x_n) = 0$	n	x_n for $J_0(x_n) = 0$	x_n for $J_1(x_n) = 0$
1	2.4048	3 8317	6	18.0711	19.6159
2	5.5201	7.0156	7	21.2116	22.7601
3	8.6537	10.1735	·8	24.3525	25 9037
4	11.7915	13.3237	9	27.4935	29.0468
5	14.9309	16.4706	10	30.6346	32.1897

TABLE IV.—VALUES OF $J_0(xi)$.

x	$J_0(xi)$	x	$J_0(xi)$	x	$J_0(xi)$
0.0	1.0000	2.0	2 2796	4.0	11.3019
0.1	1.0025	2.1	2.4463	4.1	12.3236
0.2	1.0100	2.2	2.6291	4.2	13.4425
0.3	1.0226	2.3	2.8296	4.3	14.6680
0 4	1.0404	2.4	3.0493	4.4	16.0104
0.5	1.0635	2.5	3.2898	4.5	17.4812
0.6	1.0920	2.6	3.5533	4.6	19.0926
0 7	1.1263	2.7	3.8417	4.7	20.8585
0.8	1.1665	2.8	4 1573	4.8	22.7937
0.9	1.2130	2.9	4.5027	4.9	24.9148
1.0	1.2661	3.0	4.8808	5.0	27.2399
1.1	1.3262	3.1	5.2945	5.1	29.7889
1.2	1.3937	3.2	5.7472	5.2	32.5836
1.3	1.4963	3.3	6.2426	5.3	35.6481
1 4	1.5534	3.4	6.7848	5.4	39.0088
1.5	1.6467	3.5	7.3782	5.5	42.6946
1.6	1.7500	3.6	8.0277	5.6	46.7376
1.7	1.8640	3.7	8.7386	5.7	51.1725
1.8	1.9896	3.8	9.5169	5.8	56.0381
1.9	2.1277	3.9	10.3690	5.9	61.3766

INDEX.

Bernouilli, Daniel, 7.
Bessel's Functions:
 applications to physical problems, 53–55.
 development in terms of, 55–56.
 first used, 7.
 introductory problem, 21.
 of the order zero, 23.
 of higher order, 59.
 problems, 25, 56–59.
 properties, 51–53.
 series for unity, 24, 56.
 tables, 62–63.

Conduction of heat, 7.
 differential equations for, 8, 9, 10, 13, 21, 54, 57.
 problems, 12–15, 21–25, 40, 56, 57.
Continuity, equation of, 9.
Cosine Series, 30.
 determination of the coefficients, 30.
 problems in development, 31.
Cylindrical harmonics, 52.

Differential equations, 10.
 arbitrary constants and arbitrary functions, 10.
 linear, 10.
 linear and homogeneous, 10.
 general solution, 10.
 particular solution, 10.
Dirichlet's conditions, 36.
Drumhead, vibrations of, 57, 58.

Electrical potential problems, 15, 39, 40, 43.
Ellipsoidal harmonics, 59.

Fourier, 7.
Fourier's integral, 35.
Fourier's series, 32–36.
 applications to problems in physics, 38–40.
 Dirichlet's conditions of developability, 36.
 extension of the range, 34–35.
 graphical representation, 37.
 problems in development, 33, 34.

Harmonic analysis, 7.
Harmonics:
 cylindrical, 12, 21, 25, 51–59, 62–63.
 ellipsoidal, 55.
 spherical, 7, 12, 51.
 tesseral, 51.
 toroidal, 59.
 zonal, 12, 15–21, 40, 50, 60–61.
Heat v. Conduction of heat, 7
Historical introduction, 7.

Introduction, historical and descriptive, 7, 8, 9.

Lamé, 7.
Lamé's functions, 12, 59.
Laplace, 7.

Laplace's coefficients, 12, 51.
Laplace's equation, 17, 41, 43, 51.
   in cylindrical coordinates, 10, 21.
   in spherical coordinates, 9, 12.
Laplacian, 51.
Legendre, 7.
Legendre's coefficients, 19.
Legendre's equation, 17, 40, 41, 47.

Musical strings, 7.
   differential equation for small vibrations, 7.
   problems, 39, 40.

Perry, John, 8.
Potential function in attraction:
   problems, 44, 51.

Sine series, 26.
   determination of the coefficients, 26–28.
   examples, 29.
   for unity, 12, 29.

Spherical harmonics, 7, 12, 51.
Stationary temperatures:
   problems, 21, 25, 56, 57, 59.

Tesseral harmonics, 51.
Toroidal harmonics, 59.
Tables, 60–63.

Vibrations:
   of a circular elastic membrane, 57, 58.
   of a heavy hanging string, 7.
   of a stretched elastic string, 7, 39, 40.

Zonal harmonics:
   development in terms of, 46–49.
   first used, 7.
   introductory problem, 15.
   problems, 21, 43, 44, 49, 50
   properties, 40, 43.
   short table, 19.
   special formulas, 50.
   surface and solid, 19.
   tables, 60–61.
   various forms, 45–46.

SHORT-TITLE CATALOGUE

OF THE

PUBLICATIONS

OF

JOHN WILEY & SONS,

NEW YORK.

LONDON: CHAPMAN & HALL, LIMITED.

ARRANGED UNDER SUBJECTS.

Descriptive circulars sent on application. Books marked with an asterisk (*) are sold at *net* prices only, a double asterisk (**) books sold under the rules of the American Publishers' Association at *net* prices subject to an extra charge for postage. All books are bound in cloth unless otherwise stated.

AGRICULTURE.

Armsby's Manual of Cattle-feeding.	12mo,	$1 75
Principles of Animal Nutrition.	8vo,	4 00
Budd and Hansen's American Horticultural Manual:		
Part I. Propagation, Culture, and Improvement.	12mo,	1 50
Part II. Systematic Pomology.	12mo,	1 50
Downing's Fruits and Fruit-trees of America	8vo,	5 00
Elliott's Engineering for Land Drainage.	12mo,	1 50
Practical Farm Drainage.	12mo,	1 00
Green's Principles of American Forestry.	12mo,	1 50
Grotenfelt's Principles of Modern Dairy Practice. (Woll.).	12mo,	2 00
Kemp's Landscape Gardening.	12mo,	2 50
Maynard's Landscape Gardening as Applied to Home Decoration.	12mo,	1 50
* McKay and Larsen's Principles and Practice of Butter-making	8vo,	1 50
Sanderson's Insects Injurious to Staple Crops.	12mo,	1 50
Insects Injurious to Garden Crops. (In preparation.)		
Insects Injuring Fruits. (In preparation.)		
Stockbridge's Rocks and Soils.	8vo,	2 50
Winton's Microscopy of Vegetable Foods.	8vo,	7 50
Woll's Handbook for Farmers and Dairymen.	16mo,	1 50

ARCHITECTURE.

Baldwin's Steam Heating for Buildings.	12mo,	2 50
Bashore's Sanitation of a Country House	12mo,	1 00
Berg's Buildings and Structures of American Railroads.	4to,	5 00
Birkmire's Planning and Construction of American Theatres.	8vo,	3 00
Architectural Iron and Steel.	8vo,	3 50
Compound Riveted Girders as Applied in Buildings.	8vo,	2 00
Planning and Construction of High Office Buildings.	8vo,	3 50
Skeleton Construction in Buildings.	8vo,	3 00
Brigg's Modern American School Buildings.	8vo,	4 00
Carpenter's Heating and Ventilating of Buildings.	8vo,	4 00
Freitag's Architectural Engineering.	8vo,	3 50
Fireproofing of Steel Buildings.	8vo,	2 50
French and Ives's Stereotomy.	8vo,	2 50

1

Gerhard's Guide to Sanitary House-inspection....................16mo, 1 00
    Theatre Fires and Panics....................................12mo, 1 50
*Greene's Structural Mechanics..............................8vo, 2 50
Holly's Carpenters' and Joiners' Handbook.........................18mo, 75
Johnson's Statics by Algebraic and Graphic Methods................8vo, 2 00
Kidder's Architects' and Builders' Pocket-book. Rewritten Edition. 16mo, mor., 5 00
Merrill's Stones for Building and Decoration......................8vo, 5 00
    Non-metallic Minerals: Their Occurrence and Uses..............8vo, 4 00
Monckton's Stair-building.....................................4to, 4 00
Patton's Practical Treatise on Foundations.........................8vo, 5 00
Peabody's Naval Architecture..................................8vo, 7 50
Richey's Handbook for Superintendents of Construction.........16mo, mor., 4 00
Sabin's Industrial and Artistic Technology of Paints and Varnish.......8vo, 3 00
Siebert and Biggin's Modern Stone-cutting and Masonry..............8vo, 1 50
Snow's Principal Species of Wood...............................8vo, 3 50
Sondericker's Graphic Statics with Applications to Trusses, Beams, and Arches.
                                                    8vo, 2 00
Towne's Locks and Builders' Hardware...................18mo, morocco, 3 00
Wait's Engineering and Architectural Jurisprudence..................8vo, 6 00
                                                      Sheep, 6 50
    Law of Operations Preliminary to Construction in Engineering and Archi-
      tecture...8vo, 5 00
                                                     Sheep, 5 50
    Law of Contracts..8vo, 3 00
Wood's Rustless Coatings: Corrosion and Electrolysis of Iron and Steel..8vo, 4 00
Worcester and Atkinson's Small Hospitals, Establishment and Maintenance,
    Suggestions for Hospital Architecture, with Plans for a Small Hospital.
                                                  12mo, 1 25
The World's Columbian Exposition of 1893....................Large 4to, 1 00

ARMY AND NAVY.

Bernadou's Smokeless Powder, Nitro-cellulose, and the Theory of the Cellulose
    Molecule..12mo, 2 50
* Bruff's Text-book Ordnance and Gunnery.........................8vo, 6 00
Chase's Screw Propellers and Marine Propulsion.....................8vo, 3 00
Cloke's Gunner's Examiner.....................................8vo, 1 50
Craig's Azimuth...4to, 3 50
Crehore and Squier's Polarizing Photo-chronograph..................8vo, 3 00
* Davis's Elements of Law.....................................8vo, 2 50
*   Treatise on the Military Law of United States...................8vo, 7 00
                                                      Sheep, 7 50
De Brack's Cavalry Outposts Duties. (Carr.)...............24mo, morocco, 2 00
Dietz's Soldier's First Aid Handbook....................16mo, morocco, 1 25
* Dredge's Modern French Artillery...................4to, half morocco, 15 00
Durand's Resistance and Propulsion of Ships.......................8vo, 5 00
* Dyer's Handbook of Light Artillery.............................12mo, 3 00
Eissler's Modern High Explosives...............................8vo, 4 00
* Fiebeger's Text-book on Field Fortification....................Small 8vo, 2 00
Hamilton's The Gunner's Catechism.............................18mo, 1 00
* Hoff's Elementary Naval Tactics..............................8vo, 1 50
Ingalls's Handbook of Problems in Direct Fire......................8vo, 4 00
*   Ballistic Tables...8vo, 1 50
* Lyons's Treatise on Electromagnetic Phenomena. Vols. I. and II..8vo, each, 6 00
* Mahan's Permanent Fortifications. (Mercur.)..........8vo, half morocco, 7 50
Manual for Courts-martial.............................16mo, morocco, 1 50
* Mercur's Attack of Fortified Places............................12mo, 2 00
*   Elements of the Art of War................................8vo, 4 00

Metcalf's Cost of Manufactures—And the Administration of Workshops..8vo, 5 00
*   Ordnance and Gunnery. 2 vols.............................12mo, 5 00
Murray's Infantry Drill Regulations........................18mo, paper, 10
Nixon's Adjutants' Manual.......................................24mo, 1 00
Peabody's Naval Architecture.....................................8vo, 7 50
* Phelps's Practical Marine Surveying.............................8vo, 2 50
Powell's Army Officer's Examiner................................12mo, 4 00
Sharpe's Art of Subsisting Armies in War.................18mo, morocco, 1 50
* Walke's Lectures on Explosives..................................8vo, 4 00
* Wheeler's Siege Operations and Military Mining....................8vo, 2 00
Winthrop's Abridgment of Military Law..........................12mo, 2 50
Woodhull's Notes on Military Hygiene............................16mo, 1 50
Young's Simple Elements of Navigation....................16mo, morocco. 2 00

ASSAYING.

Fletcher's Practical Instructions in Quantitative Assaying with the Blowpipe.
12mo, morocco, 1 50
Furman's Manual of Practical Assaying...........................8vo, 3 00
Lodge's Notes on Assaying and Metallurgical Laboratory Experiments....8vo, 3 00
Low's Technical Methods of Ore Analysis..........................8vo, 3 00
Miller's Manual of Assaying.....................................12mo, 1 00
Minet's Production of Aluminum and its Industrial Use. (Waldo.).....12mo, 2 50
O'Driscoll's Notes on the Treatment of Gold Ores.................8vo, 2 00
Ricketts and Miller's Notes on Assaying...........................8vo, 3 00
Robine and Lenglen's Cyanide Industry. (Le Clerc.)...............8vo,
Ulke's Modern Electrolytic Copper Refining........................8vo, 3 00
Wilson's Cyanide Processes......................................12mo, 1 50
    Chlorination Process..12mo, 1 50

ASTRONOMY.

Comstock's Field Astronomy for Engineers..........................8vo, 2 50
Craig's Azimuth...4to, 3 50
Doolittle's Treatise on Practical Astronomy........................8vo, 4 00
Gore's Elements of Geodesy..8vo, 2 50
Hayford's Text-book of Geodetic Astronomy.........................8vo, 3 00
Merriman's Elements of Precise Surveying and Geodesy..............8vo, 2 50
* Michie and Harlow's Practical Astronomy..........................8vo, 3 00
* White's Elements of Theoretical and Descriptive Astronomy........12mo, 2 00

BOTANY.

Davenport's Statistical Methods, with Special Reference to Biological Variation.
16mo, morocco, 1 25
Thomé and Bennett's Structural and Physiological Botany............16mo, 2 25
Westermaier's Compendium of General Botany. (Schneider.).........8vo, 2 00

CHEMISTRY.

Adriance's Laboratory Calculations and Specific Gravity Tables........12mo, 1 25
Allen's Tables for Iron Analysis.....................................8vo, 3 00
Arnold's Compendium of Chemistry. (Mandel.)...............Small 8vo, 3 50
Austen's Notes for Chemical Students.............................12mo, 1 50
Bernadou's Smokeless Powder.—Nitro-cellulose, and Theory of the Cellulose
    Molecule...12mo, 2 50
* Browning's Introduction to the Rarer Elements....................8vo, 1 50

3

Brush and Penfield's Manual of Determinative Mineralogy. 8vo, 4 00
Classen's Quantitative Chemical Analysis by Electrolysis. (Boltwood.)..8vo, 3 00
Cohn's Indicators and Test-papers................................12mo, 2 00
   Tests and Reagents..8vo, 3 00
Crafts's Short Course in Qualitative Chemical Analysis. (Schaeffer.)...12mo, 1 50
Dolezalek's Theory of the Lead Accumulator (Storage Battery). (Von
   Ende.)..12mo, 2 50
Drechsel's Chemical Reactions. (Merrill.).......................12mo, 1 25
Duhem's Thermodynamics and Chemistry. (Burgess.)................8vo, 4 00
Eissler's Modern High Explosives....................................8vo, 4 00
Effront's Enzymes and their Applications. (Prescott.)................8vo, 3 00
Erdmann's Introduction to Chemical Preparations. (Dunlap.).......12mo, 1 25
Fletcher's Practical Instructions in Quantitative Assaying with the Blowpipe.
                                        12mo, morocco, 1 50
Fowler's Sewage Works Analyses................................12mo, 2 00
Fresenius's Manual of Qualitative Chemical Analysis. (Wells.)........8vo, 5 00
   Manual of Qualitative Chemical Analysis. Part I. Descriptive. (Wells.) 8vo, 3 00
   System of Instruction in Quantitative Chemical Analysis. (Cohn.)
    2 vols..8vo, 12 50
Fuertes's Water and Public Health................................12mo, 1 50
Furman's Manual of Practical Assaying. ....:..............8vo, 3 00
* Getman's Exercises in Physical Chemistry........................12mo, 2 00
Gill's Gas and Fuel Analysis for Engineers.........................12mo, 1 25
Grotenfelt's Principles of Modern Dairy Practice. (Woll.)...........12mo, 2 00
Hammarsten's Text-book of Physiological Chemistry. (Mandel.).......8vo, 4 00
Helm's Principles of Mathematical Chemistry. (Morgan.)...........12mo, 1 50
Hering's Ready Reference Tables (Conversion Factors). .....16mo, morocco, 2 50
Hind's Inorganic Chemistry......................................8vo, 3 00
*   Laboratory Manual for Students 12mo, 1 00
Holleman's Text-book of Inorganic Chemistry. (Cooper.). 8vo, 2 50
   Text-book of Organic Chemistry. (Walker and Mott.)...........8vo, 2 50
*   Laboratory Manual of Organic Chemistry. (Walker.)..........12mo, 1 00
Hopkins's Oil-chemists' Handbook..................................8vo, 3 00
Jackson's Directions for Laboratory Work in Physiological Chemistry..8vo, 1 25
Keep's Cast Iron...8vo, 2 50
Ladd's Manual of Quantitative Chemical Analysis...................12mo, 1 00
Landauer's Spectrum Analysis. (Tingle.).........................8vo, 3 00
* Langworthy and Austen.   The Occurrence of Aluminium in Vegetable
   Products, Animal Products, and Natural Waters..............8vo, 2 00
Lassar-Cohn's Practical Urinary Analysis. (Lorenz.)..............12mo, 1 00
   Application of Some General Reactions to Investigations in Organic
    Chemistry. (Tingle.)......................................12mo, 1 00
Leach's The Inspection and Analysis of Food with Special Reference to State
   Control...8vo, 7 50
Löb's Electrochemistry of Organic Compounds. (Lorenz.)...........8vo, 3 00
Lodge's Notes on Assaying and Metallurgical Laboratory Experiments. ...8vo, 3 00
Low's Technical Method of Ore Analysis...........................8vo, 3 00
Lunge's Techno-chemical Analysis. (Cohn.)......................12mo, 1 00
Mandel's Handbook for Bio-chemical Laboratory 12mo, 1 50
* Martin's Laboratory Guide to Qualitative Analysis with the Blowpipe..12mo, 60
Mason's Water-supply. (Considered Principally from a Sanitary Standpoint.)
   3d Edition, Rewritten.....................................8vo, 4 00
   Examination of Water. (Chemical and Bacteriological.)........12mo, 1 25
Matthew's The Textile Fibres....................................8vo, 3 50
Meyer's Determination of Radicles in Carbon Compounds. (Tingle.). .12mo, 1 00
Miller's Manual of Assaying......................................12mo, 1 00
Minet's Production of Aluminum and its Industrial Use. (Waldo.)....12mo, 2 50
Mixter's Elementary Text-book of Chemistry......................12mo, 1 50
Morgan's Elements of Physical Chemistry.........................12mo, 3 00
   * Physical Chemistry for Electrical Engineers..................12mo, 1 50

Morse's Calculations used in Cane-sugar Factories. . . . . .16mo, morocco,   1 50
Mulliken's General Method for the Identification of Pure Organic Compounds.
    Vol. I. . . . . .Large 8vo,   5 00
O'Brine's Laboratory Guide in Chemical Analysis. 8vo,   2 00
O'Driscoll's Notes on the Treatment of Gold Ores. 8vo,   2 00
Ostwald's Conversations on Chemistry.   Part One.   (Ramsey.). 12mo,   1 50
    "   "   "   "   Part Two.   (Turnbull.). 12mo,   2 00
* Penfield's Notes on Determinative Mineralogy and Record of Mineral Tests.
                                                8vo, paper,   50
Pictet's The Alkaloids and their Chemical Constitution.   (Biddle.) 8vo,   5 00
Pinner's Introduction to Organic Chemistry.   (Austen.). 12mo,   1 50
Poole's Calorific Power of Fuels. 8vo,   3 00
Prescott and Winslow's Elements of Water Bacteriology, with Special Refer-
    ence to Sanitary Water Analysis. 12mo,   1 25
* Reisig's Guide to Piece-dyeing. 8vo, 25 00
Richards and Woodman's Air, Water, and Food from a Sanitary Stand-
    point. 8vo,   2 00
Richards's Cost of Living as Modified by Sanitary Science. 12mo,   1 00
    Cost of Food, a Study in Dietaries 12mo,   1 00
* Richards and Williams's The Dietary Computer. 8vo,   1 50
Ricketts and Russell's Skeleton Notes upon Inorganic Chemistry.   (Part I.
    Non-metallic Elements.). . . . . .8vo, morocco,   75
Ricketts and Miller's Notes on Assaying. 8vo,   3 00
Rideal's Sewage and the Bacterial Purification of Sewage. 8vo,   3 50
    Disinfection and the Preservation of Food. .8vo,   4 00
Rigg's Elementary Manual for the Chemical Laboratory. 8vo,   1 25
Robine and Lenglen's Cyanide Industry.   (Le Clerc.). 8vo,
Rostoski's Serum Diagnosis.   (Bolduan.). 12mo,   1 00
Ruddiman's Incompatibilities in Prescriptions. 8vo,   2 00
*   Whys in Pharmacy 12mo,   1 00
Sabin's Industrial and Artistic Technology of Paints and Varnish. 8vo,   3 00
Salkowski's Physiological and Pathological Chemistry.   (Orndorff.). 8vo,   2 50
Schimpf's Text-book of Volumetric Analysis. 12mo,   2 50
    Essentials of Volumetric Analysis. 12mo,   1 25
*   Qualitative Chemical Analysis. 8vo,   1 25
Spencer's Handbook for Chemists of Beet-sugar Houses. . . . .16mo, morocco,   3 00
    Handbook for Cane Sugar Manufacturers. . . . . .16mo, morocco,   3 00
Stockbridge's Rocks and Soils. 8vo,   2 50
* Tillman's Elementary Lessons in Heat. 8vo,   1 50
*   Descriptive General Chemistry. 8vo,   3 00
Treadwell's Qualitative Analysis.   (Hall.). 8vo,   3 00
    Quantitative Analysis.   (Hall.). 8vo,   4 00
Turneaure and Russell's Public Water-supplies. 8vo,   5 00
Van Deventer's Physical Chemistry for Beginners.   (Boltwood.) 12mo,   1 50
* Walke's Lectures on Explosives. 8vo,   4 00
Ware's Beet-sugar Manufacture and Refining. . . . . .Small 8vo, cloth,   4 00
Washington's Manual of the Chemical Analysis of Rocks. 8vo,   2 00
Wassermann's Immune Sera: Hæmolysins, Cytotoxins, and Precipitins.   (Bol-
    duan.). 12mo,   1 00
Well's Laboratory Guide in Qualitative Chemical Analysis. 8vo,   1 50
    Short Course in Inorganic Qualitative Chemical Analysis for Engineering
    Students. 12mo,   1 50
    Text-book of Chemical Arithmetic 12mo,   1 25
Whipple's Microscopy of Drinking-water. 8vo,   3 50
Wilson's Cyanide Processes 12mo,   1 50
    Chlorination Process. 12mo,   1 50
Winton's Microscopy of Vegetable Foods. 8vo,   7 50
Wulling's Elementary Course in Inorganic, Pharmaceutical, and Medical
    Chemistry. 12mo,   2 00

CIVIL ENGINEERING.

BRIDGES AND ROOFS. HYDRAULICS. MATERIALS OF ENGINEERING. RAILWAY ENGINEERING.

Baker's Engineers' Surveying Instruments..........................12mo, 3 00
Bixby's Graphical Computing Table................Paper 19½×24¼ inches. 25
** Burr's Ancient and Modern Engineering and the Isthmian Canal. (Postage, 27 cents additional.)...8vo, 3 50
Comstock's Field Astronomy for Engineers..........................8vo, 2 50
Davis's Elevation and Stadia Tables................................8vo, 1 00
Elliott's Engineering for Land Drainage...........................12mo, 1 50
    Practical Farm Drainage.......................................12mo, 1 00
*Fiebeger's Treatise on Civil Engineering...........................8vo, 5 00
Folwell's Sewerage. (Designing and Maintenance.)....................8vo, 3 00
Freitag's Architectural Engineering. 2d Edition, Rewritten..........8vo, 3 50
French and Ives's Stereotomy.......................................8vo, 2 50
Goodhue's Municipal Improvements.......................,..........12mo, 1 75
Goodrich's Economic Disposal of Towns' Refuse.....................8vo, 3 50
Gore's Elements of Geodesy...8vo, 2 50
Hayford's Text-book of Geodetic Astronomy..........................8vo, 3 00
Hering's Ready Reference Tables (Conversion Factors)......16mo, morocco, 2 50
Howe's Retaining Walls for Earth.................................12mo, 1 25
Johnson's (J. B.) Theory and Practice of Surveying.............Small 8vo, 4 00
Johnson's (L. J.) Statics by Algebraic and Graphic Methods...........8vo, 2 00
Laplace's Philosophical Essay on Probabilities. (Truscott and Emory.).12mo, 2 00
Mahan's Treatise on Civil Engineering. (1873.) (Wood.)............8vo, 5 00
*   Descriptive Geometry.......................................8vo, 1 50
Merriman's Elements of Precise Surveying and Geodesy............ 8vo, 2 50
Merriman and Brooks's Handbook for Surveyors...........16mo, morocco, 2 00
Nugent's Plane Surveying...8vo, 3 50
Ogden's Sewer Design...12mo, 2 00
Patton's Treatise on Civil Engineering...................8vo half leather, 7 50
Reed's Topographical Drawing and Sketching 4to, 5 00
Rideal's Sewage and the Bacterial Purification of Sewage..............8vo, 3 50
Siebert and Biggin's Modern Stone-cutting and Masonry...............8vo, 1 50
Smith's Manual of Topographical Drawing. (McMillan.)...............8vo, 2 50
Sondericker's Graphic Statics, with Applications to Trusses, Beams, and Arches. 8vo, 2 00
Taylor and Thompson's Treatise on Concrete, Plain and Reinforced.....8vo, 5 00
* Trautwine's Civil Engineer's Pocket-book................16mo, morocco, 5 00
Wait's Engineering and Architectural Jurisprudence.................8vo, 6 00
                                Sheep, 6 50
    Law of Operations Preliminary to Construction in Engineering and Architecture...8vo, 5 00
                                Sheep, 5 50
    Law of Contracts...8vo, 3 00
Warren's Stereotomy—Problems in Stone-cutting.....................8vo, 2 50
Webb's Problems in the Use and Adjustment of Engineering Instruments. 16mo, morocco, 1 25
Wilson's Topographic Surveying....................................8vo, 3 50

BRIDGES AND ROOFS.

Boller's Practical Treatise on the Construction of Iron Highway Bridges..8vo, 2 00
*   Thames River Bridge...................................4to, paper, 5 00
Burr's Course on the Stresses in Bridges and Roof Trusses, Arched Ribs, and Suspension Bridges...8vo, 3 50

6

Burr and Falk's Influence Lines for Bridge and Roof Computations....8vo, 3 00
    Design and Construction of Metallic Bridges....................8vo, 5 00
Du Bois's Mechanics of Engineering. Vol. II..................Small 4to, 10 00
Foster's Treatise on Wooden Trestle Bridges..........................4to, 5 00
Fowler's Ordinary Foundations....................................8vo, 3 50
Greene's Roof Trusses...8vo, 1 25
    Bridge Trusses...8vo, 2 50
    Arches in Wood, Iron, and Stone............................8vo, 2 50
Howe's Treatise on Arches.......................................8vo, 4 00
    Design of Simple Roof-trusses in Wood and Steel.............8vo, 2 00
Johnson, Bryan, and Turneaure's Theory and Practice in the Designing of
    Modern Framed Structures..........................Small 4to, 10 00
Merriman and Jacoby's Text-book on Roofs and Bridges:
    Part I. Stresses in Simple Trusses...........................8vo, 2 50
    Part II. Graphic Statics....................................8vo, 2 50
    Part III. Bridge Design....................................8vo, 2 50
    Part IV. Higher Structures.................................8vo, 2 50
Morison's Memphis Bridge..4to, 10 00
Waddell's De Pontibus, a Pocket-book for Bridge Engineers..16mo, morocco, 2 00
    Specifications for Steel Bridges...........................12mo, 1 25
Wright's Designing of Draw-spans. Two parts in one volume.........8vo, 3 50

HYDRAULICS.

Bazin's Experiments upon the Contraction of the Liquid Vein Issuing from
    an Orifice. (Trautwine.)...............................8vo, 2 00
Bovey's Treatise on Hydraulics...................................8vo, 5 00
Church's Mechanics of Engineering................................8vo, 6 00
    Diagrams of Mean Velocity of Water in Open Channels.......paper, 1 50
    Hydraulic Motors...8vo, 2 00
Coffin's Graphical Solution of Hydraulic Problems.........16mo, morocco, 2 50
Flather's Dynamometers, and the Measurement of Power...........12mo, 3 00
Folwell's Water-supply Engineering...............................8vo, 4 00
Frizell's Water-power...8vo, 5 00
Fuertes's Water and Public Health..............................12mo, 1 50
    Water-filtration Works...................................12mo, 2 50
Ganguillet and Kutter's General Formula for the Uniform Flow of Water in
    Rivers and Other Channels. (Hering and Trautwine.).......8vo, 4 00
Hazen's Filtration of Public Water-supply.........................8vo, 3 00
Hazlehurst's Towers and Tanks for Water-works....................8vo, 2 50
Herschel's 115 Experiments on the Carrying Capacity of Large, Riveted, Metal
    Conduits...8vo, 2 00
Mason's Water-supply. (Considered Principally from a Sanitary Standpoint.)
    8vo, 4 00
Merriman's Treatise on Hydraulics................................8vo, 5 00
* Michie's Elements of Analytical Mechanics.......................8vo, 4 00
Schuyler's Reservoirs for Irrigation, Water-power, and Domestic Water-
    supply...Large 8vo, 5 00
** Thomas and Watt's Improvement of Rivers. (Post., 44c. additional.).4to, 6 00
Turneaure and Russell's Public Water-supplies.....................8vo, 5 00
Wegmann's Design and Construction of Dams.......................4to, 5 00
    Water-supply of the City of New York from 1658 to 1895.........4to, 10 00
Williams and Hazen's Hydraulic Tables............................8vo, 1 50
Wilson's Irrigation Engineering...........................Small 8vo, 4 00
Wolff's Windmill as a Prime Mover...............................8vo, 3 00
Wood's Turbines...8vo, 2 50
    Elements of Analytical Mechanics...........................8vo, 3 00

MATERIALS OF ENGINEERING.

Baker's Treatise on Masonry Construction..........................8vo, 5 00
 Roads and Pavements.......................................8vo, 5 00
Black's United States Public Works ....Oblong 4to, 5 00
* Bovey's Strength of Materials and Theory of Structures..............8vo, 7 50
Burr's Elasticity and Resistance of the Materials of Engineering.......8vo, 7 50
Byrne's Highway Construction....................................8vo, 5 00
 Inspection of the Materials and Workmanship Employed in Construction.
                    16mo, 3 00
Church's Mechanics of Engineering................................8vo, 6 00
Du Bois's Mechanics of Engineering. Vol. I...................Small 4to, 7 50
*Eckel's Cements, Limes, and Plasters...........................8vo, 6 00
Johnson's Materials of Construction........................Large 8vo, 6 00
Fowler's Ordinary Foundations...................................8vo, 3 50
* Greene's Structural Mechanics..................................8vo, 2 50
Keep's Cast Iron..8vo, 2 50
Lanza's Applied Mechanics.......................................8vo, 7 50
Marten's Handbook on Testing Materials. (Henning.) 2 vols........8vo, 7 50
Maurer's Technical Mechanics....................................8vo, 4 00
Merrill's Stones for Building and Decoration.....................8vo, 5 00
Merriman's Mechanics of Materials...............................8vo, 5 00
 Strength of Materials......................................12mo, 1 00
Metcalf's Steel. A Manual for Steel-users......................12mo, 2 00
Patton's Practical Treatise on Foundations.......................8vo, 5 00
Richardson's Modern Asphalt Pavements...........................8vo, 3 00
Richey's Handbook for Superintendents of Construction.........16mo, mor., 4 00
Rockwell's Roads and Pavements in France.......................12mo, 1 25
Sabin's Industrial and Artistic Technology of Paints and Varnish........8vo, 3 00
Smith's Materials of Machines...................................12mo, 1 00
Snow's Principal Species of Wood................................8vo, 3 50
Spalding's Hydraulic Cement....................................12mo, 2 00
 Text-book on Roads and Pavements..........................12mo, 2 00
Taylor and Thompson's Treatise on Concrete, Plain and Reinforced......8vo, 5 00
Thurston's Materials of Engineering. 3 Parts....................8vo, 8 00
 Part I. Non-metallic Materials of Engineering and Metallurgy.....8vo, 2 00
 Part II. Iron and Steel..................................8vo, 3 50
 Part III. A Treatise on Brasses, Bronzes, and Other Alloys and their
   Constituents...8vo, 2 50
Thurston's Text-book of the Materials of Construction.............8vo, 5 00
Tillson's Street Pavements and Paving Materials...................8vo, 4 00
Waddell's De Pontibus. (A Pocket-book for Bridge Engineers.)..16mo, mor., 2 00
 Specifications for Steel Bridges...........................12mo, 1 25
Wood's (De V.) Treatise on the Resistance of Materials, and an Appendix on
 the Preservation of Timber.................................8vo, 2 00
Wood's (De V.) Elements of Analytical Mechanics..................8vo, 3 00
Wood's (M. P.) Rustless Coatings: Corrosion and Electrolysis of Iron and
 Steel..8vo, 4 00

RAILWAY ENGINEERING.

Andrew's Handbook for Street Railway Engineers.....3x5 inches, morocco, 1 25
Berg's Buildings and Structures of American Railroads 4to, 5 00
Brook's Handbook of Street Railroad Location. ....16mo, morocco, 1 50
Butt's Civil Engineer's Field-book.......................16mo, morocco, 2 50
Crandall's Transition Curve.............................16mo, morocco, 1 50
 Railway and Other Earthwork Tables........................8vo, 1 50
Dawson's "Engineering" and Electric Traction Pocket-book..16mo, morocco, 5 00

Dredge's History of the Pennsylvania Railroad: (1879).............Paper, 5 00
* Drinker's Tunnelling, Explosive Compounds, and Rock Drills.4to, half mor., 25 00
Fisher's Table of Cubic Yards.................................Cardboard, 25
Godwin's Railroad Engineers' Field-book and Explorers' Guide...16mo, mor., 2 50
Howard's Transition Curve Field-book....................16mo, morocco, 1 50
Hudson's Tables for Calculating the Cubic Contents of Excavations and Em-
      bankments..8vo, 1 00
Molitor and Beard's Manual for Resident Engineers................16mo, 1 00
Nagle's Field Manual for Railroad Engineers..............16mo, morocco, 3 00
Philbrick's Field Manual for Engineers...................16mo, morocco, 3 00
Searles's Field Engineering..............................16mo, morocco, 3 00
    Railroad Spiral......................................16mo, morocco, 1 50
Taylor's Prismoidal Formulæ and Earthwork.......................8vo, 1 50
* Trautwine's Method of Calculating the Cube Contents of Excavations and
      Embankments by the Aid of Diagrams......................8vo, 2 00
The Field Practice of Laying Out Circular Curves for Railroads.
                            12mo, morocco, 2 50
    Cross-section Sheet...................................Paper, 25
Webb's Railroad Construction..........................16mo, morocco, 5 00
Wellington's Economic Theory of the Location of Railways.......Small 8vo, 5 00

DRAWING.

Barr's Kinematics of Machinery....................................8vo, 2 50
* Bartlett's Mechanical Drawing...................................8vo, 3 00
*   "   "   Abridged Ed. 8vo, 1 50
Coolidge's Manual of Drawing.............................8vo, paper 1 00
Coolidge and Freeman's Elements of General Drafting for Mechanical Engi-
    neers..Oblong 4to, 2 50
Durley's Kinematics of Machines..................................8vo, 4 00
Emch's Introduction to Projective Geometry and its Applications.......8vo, 2 50
Hill's Text-book on Shades and Shadows, and Perspective.............8vo, 2 00
Jamison's Elements of Mechanical Drawing.........................8vo, 2 50
    Advanced Mechanical Drawing...............................8vo, 2 00
Jones's Machine Design:
    Part I.   Kinematics of Machinery...........................8vo, 1 50
    Part II.   Form, Strength, and Proportions of Parts..............8vo, 3 00
MacCord's Elements of Descriptive Geometry.......................8vo, 3 00
    Kinematics; or, Practical Mechanism.........................8vo, 5 00
    Mechanical Drawing.......................................4to, 4 00
    Velocity Diagrams...8vo, 1 50
MacLeod's Descriptive Geometry.............................Small 8vo, 1 50
* Mahan's Descriptive Geometry and Stone-cutting...................8vo, 1 50
    Industrial Drawing. (Thompson.).............................8vo, 3 50
Moyer's Descriptive Geometry.....................................8vo, 2 00
Reed's Topographical Drawing and Sketching........................4to, 5 00
Reid's Course in Mechanical Drawing..............................8vo, 2 00
    Text-book of Mechanical Drawing and Elementary Machine Design.8vo, 3 00
Robinson's Principles of Mechanism...............................8vo, 3 00
Schwamb and Merrill's Elements of Mechanism.....................8vo, 3 00
Smith's (R. S.) Manual of Topographical Drawing. (McMillan.)......8vo, 2 50
Smith (A. W.) and Marx's Machine Design.........................8vo, 3 00
Warren's Elements of Plane and Solid Free-hand Geometrical Drawing.12mo, 1 00
    Drafting Instruments and Operations..........................12mo, 1 25
    Manual of Elementary Projection Drawing.....................12mo, 1 50
    Manual of Elementary Problems in the Linear Perspective of Form and
      Shadow...12mo, 1 00
    Plane Problems in Elementary Geometry 12mo, 1 25
9

Warren's Primary Geometry..12mo, 75
    Elements of Descriptive Geometry, Shadows, and Perspective.......8vo, 3 50
    General Problems of Shades and Shadows.......................8vo, 3 00
    Elements of Machine Construction and Drawing..................8vo, 7 50
    Problems, Theorems, and Examples in Descriptive Geometry.......8vo, 2 50
Weisbach's Kinematics and Power of Transmission. (Hermann and
    Klein.)...8vo, 5 0o
Whelpley's Practical Instruction in the Art of Letter Engraving. 12mo, 2 00
Wilson's (H. M.) Topographic Surveying............................8vo, 3 50
Wilson's (V. T.) Free-hand Perspective.............................8vo, 2 50
Wilson's (V. T.) Free-hand Lettering..............................8vo, 1 00
Woolf's Elementary Course in Descriptive Geometry............Large 8vo, 3 00

ELECTRICITY AND PHYSICS.

Anthony and Brackett's Text-book of Physics. (Magie.).........Small 8vo, 3 00
Anthony's Lecture-notes on the Theory of Electrical Measurements....12mo, 1 00
Benjamin's History of Electricity.................................8vo, 3 00
    Voltaic Cell...8vo, 3 00
Classen's Quantitative Chemical Analysis by Electrolysis. (Boltwood.).8vo, 3 00
Crehore and Squier's Polarizing Photo-chronograph..................8vo, 3 00
Dawson's "Engineering" and Electric Traction Pocket-book.16mo, morocco, 5 00
Dolezalek's Theory of the Lead Accumulator (Storage Battery). (Von
    Ende.)...12mo, 2 50
Duhem's Thermodynamics and Chemistry. (Burgess.)................8vo, 4 00
Flather's Dynamometers, and the Measurement of Power...........12mo, 3 00
Gilbert's De Magnete. (Mottelay.)................................8vo, 2 50
Hanchett's Alternating Currents Explained..........................12mo, 1 00
Hering's Ready Reference Tables (Conversion Factors)......16mo, morocco, 2 50
Holman's Precision of Measurements................................8vo, 2 00
    Telescopic Mirror-scale Method, Adjustments, and Tests....Large 8vo, 75
Kinzbrunner's Testing of Continuous-current Machines...............8vo, 2 00
Landauer's Spectrum Analysis. (Tingle.).........................8vo, 3 00
Le Chatelier's High-temperature Measurements. (Boudouard—Burgess.) 12mo, 3 00
Löb's Electrochemistry of Organic Compounds. (Lorenz.)............8vo, 3 00
* Lyons's Treatise on Electromagnetic Phenomena. Vols. I. and II. 8vo, each, 6 00
* Michie's Elements of Wave Motion Relating to Sound and Light.......8vo, 4 00
Niaudet's Elementary Treatise on Electric Batteries. (Fishback.). 12mo, 2 50
* Rosenberg's Electrical Engineering. (Haldane Gee—Kinzbrunner.). ..8vo, 1 50
Ryan, Norris, and Hoxie's Electrical Machinery. Vol. I..............8vo, 2 50
Thurston's Stationary Steam-engines...............................8vo, 2 50
* Tillman's Elementary Lessons in Heat............................8vo, 1 50
Tory and Pitcher's Manual of Laboratory Physics...............Small 8vo, 2 00
Ulke's Modern Electrolytic Copper Refining........................8vo, 3 00

LAW.

* Davis's Elements of Law..8vo, 2 50
*   Treatise on the Military Law of United States...................8vo, 7 00
*   Sheep, 7 50
Manual for Courts-martial...............................16mo, morocco, 1 50
Wait's Engineering and Architectural Jurisprudence..................8vo, 6 00
                                          Sheep, 6 50
    Law of Operations Preliminary to Construction in Engineering and Archi-
        tecture...8vo, 5 00
                                          Sheep, 5 50
    Law of Contracts...8vo, 3 00
Winthrop's Abridgment of Military Law...........................12mo, 2 50

MANUFACTURES.

Bernadou's Smokeless Powder—Nitro-cellulose and Theory of the Cellulose
    Molecule..12mo, 2 50
Bolland's Iron Founder.....................................12mo, 2 50
    "The Iron Founder," Supplement...........................12mo, 2 50
    Encyclopedia of Founding and Dictionary of Foundry Terms Used in the
    Practice of Moulding....................................12mo, 3 00
Eissler's Modern High Explosives..............................8vo, 4 00
Effront's Enzymes and their Applications. (Prescott.)..............8vo, 3 00
Fitzgerald's Boston Machinist................................12mo, 1 00
Ford's Boiler Making for Boiler Makers........................18mo, 1 00
Hopkin's Oil-chemists' Handbook..............................8vo, 3 00
Keep's Cast Iron..8vo, 2 50
Leach's The Inspection and Analysis of Food with Special Reference to State
    Control..Large 8vo, 7 50
Matthews's The Textile Fibres................................8vo, 3 50
Metcalf's Steel. A Manual for Steel-users....................12mo, 2 00
Metcalfe's Cost of Manufactures—And the Administration of Workshops.8vo, 5 00
Meyer's Modern Locomotive Construction........................4to, 10 00
Morse's Calculations used in Cane-sugar Factories..........16mo, morocco, 1 50
* Reisig's Guide to Piece-dyeing.............................8vo, 25 00
Sabin's Industrial and Artistic Technology of Paints and Varnish.......8vo, 3 00
Smith's Press-working of Metals...............................8vo, 3 00
Spalding's Hydraulic Cement.................................12mo, 2 00
Spencer's Handbook for Chemists of Beet-sugar Houses..... 16mo, morocco, 3 00
    Handbook for Cane Sugar Manufacturers..............16mo, morocco, 3 00
Taylor and Thompson's Treatise on Concrete, Plain and Reinforced.....8vo, 5 00
Thurston's Manual of Steam-boilers, their Designs, Construction and Opera-
    tion...8vo, 5 00
* Walke's Lectures on Explosives..............................8vo, 4 00
Ware's Beet-sugar Manufacture and Refining..................Small 8vo, 4 00
West's American Foundry Practice.............................12mo, 2 50
    Moulder's Text-book.....................................12mo, 2 50
Wolff's Windmill as a Prime Mover 8vo, 3 00
Wood's Rustless Coatings: Corrosion and Electrolysis of Iron and Steel..8vo, 4 00

MATHEMATICS.

Baker's Elliptic Functions....................................8vo, 1 50
* Bass's Elements of Differential Calculus....................12mo, 4 00
Briggs's Elements of Plane Analytic Geometry.................12mo, 1 00
Compton's Manual of Logarithmic Computations................12mo, 1 50
Davis's Introduction to the Logic of Algebra...................8vo, 1 50
* Dickson's College Algebra............................Large 12mo, 1 50
*   Introduction to the Theory of Algebraic Equations........Large 12mo, 1 25
Emch's Introduction to Projective Geometry and its Applications.......8vo, 2 50
Halsted's Elements of Geometry...............................8vo, 1 75
    Elementary Synthetic Geometry..........................8vo, 1 50
    Rational Geometry.....................................12mo, 1 75
* Johnson's (J. B.) Three-place Logarithmic Tables: Vest-pocket size.paper, 15
                                    100 copies for 5 00
*   Mounted on heavy cardboard, 8 × 10 inches, 25
                                    10 copies for 2 00
Johnson's (W. W.) Elementary Treatise on Differential Calculus..Small 8vo, 3 00
Johnson's (W. W.) Elementary Treatise on the Integral Calculus.Small 8vo, 1 50

11

Johnson's (W. W.) Curve Tracing in Cartesian Co-ordinates.........12mo, 1 00
Johnson's (W. W.) Treatise on Ordinary and Partial Differential Equations.
                                                             Small 8vo, 3 50
Johnson's (W. W.) Theory of Errors and the Method of Least Squares.12mo, 1 50
* Johnson's (W. W.) Theoretical Mechanics.......................12mo, 3 00
Laplace's Philosophical Essay on Probabilities. (Truscott and Emory.).12mo, 2 00
* Ludlow and Bass. Elements of Trigonometry and Logarithmic and Other
      Tables...8vo, 3 00
    Trigonometry and Tables published separately..................Each, 2 00
* Ludlow's Logarithmic and Trigonometric Tables...................8vo, 1 00
Mathematical Monographs. Edited by Mansfield Merriman and Robert
      S. Woodward...............................Octavo, each 1 00
    No. 1. History of Modern Mathematics, by David Eugene Smith.
    No. 2. Synthetic Projective Geometry, by George Bruce Halsted.
    No. 3. Determinants, by Laenas Gifford Weld. No. 4. Hyper-
    bolic Functions, by James McMahon. No. 5. Harmonic Func-
    tions, by William E. Byerly. No. 6. Grassmann's Space Analysis,
    by Edward W. Hyde. No. 7. Probability and Theory of Errors,
    by Robert S. Woodward. No. 8. Vector Analysis and Quaternions,
    by Alexander Macfarlane. No. 9. Differential Equations, by
    William Woolsey Johnson. No. 10. The Solution of Equations,
    by Mansfield Merriman. No. 11. Functions of a Complex Variable,
    by Thomas S. Fiske.
Maurer's Technical Mechanics.....................................8vo, 4 00
Merriman and Woodward's Higher Mathematics.....................8vo, 5 00
Merriman's Method of Least Squares........................... . .8vo, 2 00
Rice and Johnson's Elementary Treatise on the Differential Calculus..Sm. 8vo, 3 00
    Differential and Integral Calculus. 2 vols. in one..........Small 8vo, 2 50
Wood's Elements of Co-ordinate Geometry.........................8vo, 2 00
    Trigonometry: Analytical, Plane, and Spherical 12mo, 1 00

MECHANICAL ENGINEERING.

MATERIALS OF ENGINEERING, STEAM-ENGINES AND BOILERS.

Bacon's Forge Practice...12mo, 1 50
Baldwin's Steam Heating for Buildings............................12mo, 2 50
Barr's Kinematics of Machinery...................................8vo, 2 50
* Bartlett's Mechanical Drawing...................................8vo, 3 00
*   "   "   "   Abridged Ed........................8vo, 1 50
Benjamin's Wrinkles and Recipes.................................12mo, 2 00
Carpenter's Experimental Engineering............................8vo, 6 00
    Heating and Ventilating Buildings............................8vo, 4 00
Cary's Smoke Suppression in Plants using Bituminous Coal. (In Prepara-
    tion.)
Clerk's Gas and Oil Engine.................................Small 8vo, 4 00
Coolidge's Manual of Drawing............................8vo, paper, 1 00
Coolidge and Freeman's Elements of General Drafting for Mechanical En-
    gineers...Oblong 4to, 2 50
Cromwell's Treatise on Toothed Gearing..........................12mo, 1 50
    Treatise on Belts and Pulleys................................12mo, 1 50
Durley's Kinematics of Machines.................................8vo, 4 00
Flather's Dynamometers and the Measurement of Power............12mo, 3 00
    Rope Driving...12mo, 2 00
Gill's Gas and Fuel Analysis for Engineers........................12mo, 1 25
Hall's Car Lubrication...12mo, 1 00
Hering's Ready Reference Tables (Conversion Factors)......16mo, morocco, 2 50

Hutton's The Gas Engine. 8vo, 5 00
Jamison's Mechanical Drawing. 8vo, 2 50
Jones's Machine Design:
    Part I. Kinematics of Machinery. 8vo, 1 50
    Part II. Form, Strength, and Proportions of Parts. 8vo, 3 00
Kent's Mechanical Engineers' Pocket-book. . . . . .16mo, morocco, 5 00
Kerr's Power and Power Transmission. 8vo, 2 00
Leonard's Machine Shop, Tools, and Methods. 8vo, 4 00
* Lorenz's Modern Refrigerating Machinery. (Pope, Haven, and Dean.). .8vo, 4 00
MacCord's Kinematics; or, Practical Mechanism. 8vo, 5 00
    Mechanical Drawing. 4to, 4 00
    Velocity Diagrams. 8vo, 1 50
MacFarland's Standard Reduction Factors for Gases. 8vo, 1 50
Mahan's Industrial Drawing. (Thompson.). 8vo, 3 50
Poole's Calorific Power of Fuels. 8vo, 3 00
Reid's Course in Mechanical Drawing. 8vo, 2 00
    Text-book of Mechanical Drawing and Elementary Machine Design.8vo, 3 00
Richard's Compressed Air. 12mo, 1 50
Robinson's Principles of Mechanism. 8vo, 3 00
Schwamb and Merrill's Elements of Mechanism. 8vo, 3 00
Smith's (O.) Press-working of Metals. 8vo, 3 00
Smith (A. W.) and Marx's Machine Design. 8vo, 3 00
Thurston's Treatise on Friction and Lost Work in Machinery and Mill
    Work. 8vo, 3 00
    Animal as a Machine and Prime Motor, and the Laws of Energetics.12mo, 1 00
Warren's Elements of Machine Construction and Drawing. 8vo, 7 50
Weisbach's Kinematics and the Power of Transmission. (Herrmann—
    Klein.). 8vo, 5 00
    Machinery of Transmission and Governors. (Herrmann—Klein.). .8vo, 5 00
Wolff's Windmill as a Prime Mover. 8vo, 3 00
Wood's Turbines. 8vo, 2 50

MATERIALS OF ENGINEERING.

* Bovey's Strength of Materials and Theory of Structures. 8vo, 7 50
Burr's Elasticity and Resistance of the Materials of Engineering. 6th Edition.
    Reset. 8vo, 7 50
Church's Mechanics of Engineering. 8vo, 6 00
* Greene's Structural Mechanics. 8vo, 2 50
Johnson's Materials of Construction. 8vo, 6 00
Keep's Cast Iron. 8vo, 2 50
Lanza's Applied Mechanics. 8vo, 7 50
Martens's Handbook on Testing Materials. (Henning.). 8vo, 7 50
Maurer's Technical Mechanics. 8vo, 4 00
Merriman's Mechanics of Materials. 8vo, 5 00
    Strength of Materials. 12mo, 1 00
Metcalf's Steel. A manual for Steel-users. 12mo, 2 00
Sabin's Industrial and Artistic Technology of Paints and Varnish. 8vo, 3 00
Smith's Materials of Machines. 12mo, 1 00
Thurston's Materials of Engineering. .3 vols., 8vo, 8 00
    Part II. Iron and Steel. 8vo, 3 50
    Part III. A Treatise on Brasses, Bronzes, and Other Alloys and their
        Constituents. 8vo, 2 50
    Text-book of the Materials of Construction. .8vo, 5 00
Wood's (De V.) Treatise on the Resistance of Materials and an Appendix on
    the Preservation of Timber. 8vo, 2 00

Wood's (De V.) Elements of Analytical Mechanics....................8vo, 3 00
Wood's (M. P.) Rustless Coatings: Corrosion and Electrolysis of Iron and
    Steel...8vo, 4 00

STEAM-ENGINES AND BOILERS.

Berry's Temperature-entropy Diagram.............................12mo, 1 25
Carnot's Reflections on the Motive Power of Heat. (Thurston.)......12mo, 1 50
Dawson's "Engineering" and Electric Traction Pocket-book... 16mo, mor., 5 00
Ford's Boiler Making for Boiler Makers............................18mo, 1 00
Goss's Locomotive Sparks...8vo, 2 00
Hemenway's Indicator Practice and Steam-engine Economy..........12mo, 2 00
Hutton's Mechanical Engineering of Power Plants...................8vo, 5 00
    Heat and Heat-engines..8vo, 5 00
Kent's Steam boiler Economy......................................8vo, 4 00
Kneass's Practice and Theory of the Injector.......................8vo, 1 50
MacCord's Slide-valves..8vo, 2 00
Meyer's Modern Locomotive Construction............................4to, 10 00
Peabody's Manual of the Steam-engine Indicator...................12mo, 1 50
    Tables of the Properties of Saturated Steam and Other Vapors 8vo, 1 00
    Thermodynamics of the Steam-engine and Other Heat-engines......8vo, 5 00
    Valve-gears for Steam-engines.................................8vo, 2 50
Peabody and Miller's Steam-boilers................................8vo, 4 00
Pray's Twenty Years with the Indicator........................Large 8vo, 2 50
Pupin's Thermodynamics of Reversible Cycles in Gases and Saturated Vapors.
    (Osterberg.)...12mo, 1 25
Reagan's Locomotives: Simple Compound, and Electric.............12mo, 2 50
Rontgen's Principles of Thermodynamics. (Du Bois.)...............8vo, 5 00
Sinclair's Locomotive Engine Running and Management.............12mo, 2 00
Smart's Handbook of Engineering Laboratory Practice..............12mo, 2 50
Snow's Steam-boiler Practice......................................8vo, 3 00
Spangler's Valve-gears..8vo, 2 50
    Notes on Thermodynamics.....................................12mo, 1 00
Spangler, Greene, and Marshall's Elements of Steam-engineering 8vo, 3 00
Thurston's Handy Tables...8vo, 1 50
    Manual of the Steam-engine............................2 vols., 8vo, 10 00
    Part I. History, Structure, and Theory.........................8vo, 6 00
    Part II. Design, Construction, and Operation...................8vo, 6 00
    Handbook of Engine and Boiler Trials, and the Use of the Indicator and
        the Prony Brake...8vo, 5 00
    Stationary Steam-engines.....................................8vo, 2 50
    Steam-boiler Explosions in Theory and in Practice 12mo, 1 50
    Manual of Steam-boilers, their Designs, Construction, and Operation.....8vo, 5 00
Weisbach's Heat, Steam, and Steam-engines. (Du Bois.)............8vo, 5 00
Whitham's Steam-engine Design....................................8vo, 5 00
Wilson's Treatise on Steam-boilers. (Flather.)....................16mo, 2 50
Wood's Thermodynamics, Heat Motors, and Refrigerating Machines...8vo, 4 00

MECHANICS AND MACHINERY.

Barr's Kinematics of Machinery....................................8vo, 2 50
* Bovey's Strength of Materials and Theory of Structures 8vo, 7 50
Chase's The Art of Pattern-making................................12mo, 2 50
Church's Mechanics of Engineering................................8vo, 6 00
    Notes and Examples in Mechanics.............................8vo, 2 00
Compton's First Lessons in Metal-working.........................12mo, 1 50
Compton and De Groodt's The Speed Lathe........................12mo, 1 50

Cromwell's Treatise on Toothed Gearing...........................12mo, 1 50

    Treatise on Belts and Pulleys..................................12mo, 1 50

Dana's Text-book of Elementary Mechanics for Colleges and Schools..12mo, 1 50

Dingey's Machinery Pattern Making 12mo, 2 00

Dredge's Record of the Transportation Exhibits Building of the World's

        Columbian Exposition of 1893..................4to half morocco, 5 00

Du Bois's Elementary Principles of Mechanics:

    Vol. I. Kinematics...8vo, 3 50

    Vol. II. Statics...8vo, 4 00

    Mechanics of Engineering. Vol. I.......................Small 4to, 7 50

                     Vol. II......................Small 4to, 10 00

Durley's Kinematics of Machines.................................8vo, 4 00

Fitzgerald's Boston Machinist....................................16mo, 1 00

Flather's Dynamometers, and the Measurement of Power...........12mo, 3 00

    Rope Driving...12mo, 2 00

Goss's Locomotive Sparks..8vo, 2 00

* Greene's Structural Mechanics...................................8vo, 2 50

Hall's Car Lubrication...12mo, 1 00

Holly's Art of Saw Filing..18mo, 75

James's Kinematics of a Point and the Rational Mechanics of a Particle.

                                  Small 8vo, 2 00

* Johnson's (W. W.) Theoretical Mechanics........................12mo, 3 00

Johnson's (L. J.) Statics by Graphic and Algebraic Methods...........8vo, 2 00

Jones's Machine Design:

    Part I. Kinematics of Machinery............................8vo, 1 50

    Part II. Form, Strength, and Proportions of Parts..............8vo, 3 00

Kerr's Power and Power Transmission.............................8vo, 2 00

Lanza's Applied Mechanics.......................................8vo, 7 50

Leonard's Machine Shop, Tools, and Methods......................8vo, 4 00

* Lorenz's Modern Refrigerating Machinery. (Pope, Haven, and Dean.).8vo, 4 00

MacCord's Kinematics; or, Practical Mechanism....................8vo, 5 00

    Velocity Diagrams...8vo, 1 50

Maurer's Technical Mechanics....................................8vo, 4 00

Merriman's Mechanics of Materials...............................8vo, 5 00

*   Elements of Mechanics......................................12mo, 1 00

* Michie's Elements of Analytical Mechanics.......................8vo, 4 00

Reagan's Locomotives: Simple, Compound, and Electric............12mo, 2 50

Reid's Course in Mechanical Drawing.............................8vo, 2 00

    Text-book of Mechanical Drawing and Elementary Machine Design.8vo, 3 00

Richards's Compressed Air.......................................12mo, 1 50

Robinson's Principles of Mechanism..............................8vo, 3 00

Ryan, Norris, and Hoxie's Electrical Machinery. Vol. I..............8vo, 2 50

Schwamb and Merrill's Elements of Mechanism....................8vo, 3 00

Sinclair's Locomotive-engine Running and Management............12mo, 2 00

Smith's (O.) Press-working of Metals 8vo, 3 00

Smith's (A. W.) Materials of Machines............................12mo, 1 00

Smith (A. W.) and Marx's Machine Design.........................8vo, 3 00

Spangler, Greene, and Marshall's Elements of Steam-engineering........8vo, 3 00

Thurston's Treatise on Friction and Lost Work in Machinery and Mill

    Work...8vo, 3 00

    Animal as a Machine and Prime Motor, and the Laws of Energetics.

                                    12mo, 1 00

Warren's Elements of Machine Construction and Drawing............8vo, 7 50

Weisbach's Kinematics and Power of Transmission. (Herrmann—Klein.).8vo, 5 00

    Machinery of Transmission and Governors. (Herrmann—Klein.).8vo, 5 00

Wood's Elements of Analytical Mechanics.........................8vo, 3 00

    Principles of Elementary Mechanics..........................12mo, 1 25

    Turbines..8vo, 2 50

The World's Columbian Exposition of 1893 ....4to, 1 00

METALLURGY.

Egleston's Metallurgy of Silver, Gold, and Mercury:
    Vol. I.   Silver. 8vo, 7 50
    Vol. II. Gold and Mercury.................................8vo, 7 50
** Iles's Lead-smelting. (Postage 9 cents additional.)............12mo, 2 50
Keep's Cast Iron...8vo, 2 50
Kunhardt's Practice of Ore Dressing in Europe......................8vo, 1 50
Le Chatelier's High-temperature Measurements. (Boudouard—Burgess.)12mo, 3 00
Metcalf's Steel. A Manual for Steel-users.......................12mo, 2 00
Minet's Production of Aluminum and its Industrial Use. (Waldo.)....12mo, 2 50
Robine and Lenglen's Cyanide Industry. (Le Clerc.)................8vo,
Smith's Materials of Machines.................................12mo, 1 00
Thurston's Materials of Engineering. In Three Parts. 8vo, 8 00
    Part II.   Iron and Steel..................................8vo, 3 50
    Part III.   A Treatise on Brasses, Bronzes, and Other Alloys and their
              Constituents. 8vo, 2 50
Ulke's Modern Electrolytic Copper Refining.......................8vo, 3 00

MINERALOGY.

Barringer's Description of Minerals of Commercial Value. Oblong, morocco, 2 50
Boyd's Resources of Southwest Virginia...........................8vo, 3 00
    Map of Southwest Virignia....................Pocket-book form. 2 00
Brush's Manual of Determinative Mineralogy. (Penfield.)............8vo, 4 00
Chester's Catalogue of Minerals..........................8vo, paper, 1 00
                                                    Cloth, 1 25
    Dictionary of the Names of Minerals........................8vo, 3 50
Dana's System of Mineralogy. ....Large 8vo, half leather, 12 50
    First Appendix to Dana's New "System of Mineralogy." .....Large 8vo, 1 00
    Text-book of Mineralogy..................................8vo, 4 00
    Minerals and How to Study Them 12mo, 1 50
    Catalogue of American Localities of Minerals...............Large 8vo, 1 00
    Manual of Mineralogy and Petrography......................12mo, 2 00
Douglas's Untechnical Addresses on Technical Subjects. 12mo, 1 00
Eakle's Mineral Tables.......................................8vo, 1 25
Egleston's Catalogue of Minerals and Synonyms....................8vo, 2 50
Hussak's The Determination of Rock-forming Minerals. (Smith.). Small 8vo, 2 00
Merrill's Non-metallic Minerals: Their Occurrence and Uses. 8vo, 4 00
* Penfield's Notes on Determinative Mineralogy and Record of Mineral Tests.
                                                8vo, paper, 50
Rosenbusch's Microscopical Physiography of the Rock-making Minerals.
    (Iddings.)..8vo, 5 00
* Tillman's Text-book of Important Minerals and Rocks. 8vo, 2 00

MINING.

Beard's Ventilation of Mines....................................12mo, 2 50
Boyd's Resources of Southwest Virginia..........................8vo, 3 00
    Map of Southwest Virginia......................Pocket-book form. 2 00
Douglas's Untechnical Addresses on Technical Subjects. 12mo, 1 00
* Drinker's Tunneling, Explosive Compounds, and Rock Drills. .4to, hf. mor., 25 00
Eissler's Modern High Explosives................................8vo, 4 00

Fowler's Sewage Works Analyses.................................12mo, 2 00
Goodyear's Coal-mines of the Western Coast of the United States......12mo, 2 50
Ihlseng's Manual of Mining...8vo, 5 00
** lles's Lead-smelting. (Postage 9c. additional.)..................12mo, 2 50
Kunhardt's Practice of Ore Dressing in Europe.......................8vo, 1 50
O'Driscoll's Notes on the Treatment of Gold Ores...................8vo, 2 00
Robine and Lenglen's Cyanide Industry. (Le Clerc.)................8vo,
* Walke's Lectures on Explosives...................................8vo, 4 00
Wilson's Cyanide Processes...12mo, 1 50
    Chlorination Process...12mo, 1 50
    Hydraulic and Placer Mining....................................12mo, 2 00
    Treatise on Practical and Theoretical Mine Ventilation..........12mo, 1 25

SANITARY SCIENCE.

Bashore's Sanitation of a Country House............................12mo, 1 00
Folwell's Sewerage. (Designing, Construction, and Maintenance.)......8vo, 3 00
    Water-supply Engineering.......................................8vo, 4 00
Fuertes's Water and Public Health..................................12mo, 1 50
    Water-filtration Works...12mo, 2 50
Gerhard's Guide to Sanitary House-inspection.......................16mo, 1 00
Goodrich's Economic Disposal of Town's Refuse................Demy 8vo, 3 50
Hazen's Filtration of Public Water-supplies.........................8vo, 3 00
Leach's The Inspection and Analysis of Food with Special Reference to State
    Control..8vo, 7 50
Mason's Water-supply. (Considered principally from a Sanitary Standpoint) 8vo, 4 00
    Examination of Water. (Chemical and Bacteriological.).........12mo, 1 25
Ogden's Sewer Design..12mo, 2 00
Prescott and Winslow's Elements of Water Bacteriology, with Special Refer-
    ence to Sanitary Water Analysis...............................12mo, 1 25
* Price's Handbook on Sanitation...................................12mo, 1 50
Richards's Cost of Food. A Study in Dietaries.....................12mo, 1 00
    Cost of Living as Modified by Sanitary Science.................12mo, 1 00
Richards and Woodman's Air, Water, and Food from a Sanitary Stand-
    point...8vo, 2 00
* Richards and Williams's The Dietary Computer.....................8vo, 1 50
Rideal's Sewage and Bacterial Purification of Sewage...............8vo, 3 50
Turneaure and Russell's Public Water-supplies......................8vo, 5 00
Von Behring's Suppression of Tuberculosis. (Bolduan.)............12mo, 1 00
Whipple's Microscopy of Drinking-water.............................8vo, 3 50
Winton's Microscopy of Vegetable Foods.............................8vo, 7 50
Woodhull's Notes on Military Hygiene...............................16mo, 1 50

MISCELLANEOUS.

De Fursac's Manual of Psychiatry. (Rosanoff and Collins.)....Large 12mo, 2 50
Emmons's Geological Guide-book of the Rocky Mountain Excursion of the
    International Congress of Geologists.....................Large 8vo, 1 50
Ferrel's Popular Treatise on the Winds..............................8vo, 4 00
Haines's American Railway Management..............................12mo, 2 50
Mott's Fallacy of the Present Theory of Sound......................16mo, 1 00
Ricketts's History of Rensselaer Polytechnic Institute, 1824–1894..Small 8vo, 3 00
Rostoski's Serum Diagnosis. (Bolduan.)............................12mo, 1 00
Rotherham's Emphasized New Testament......................Large 8vo, 2 00

17

Steel's Treatise on the Diseases of the Dog. 8vo, 3 50
The World's Columbian Exposition of 1893 . . . . .4to, 1 00
Von Behring's Suppression of Tuberculosis. (Bolduan.). 12mo, 1 00
Winslow's Elements of Applied Microscopy. 12mo, 1 50
Worcester and Atkinson. Small Hospitals, Establishment and Maintenance;
    Suggestions for Hospital Architecture : Plans for Small Hospital. 12mo, 1 25

HEBREW AND CHALDEE TEXT-BOOKS.

Green's Elementary Hebrew Grammar. 12mo, 1 25
    Hebrew Chrestomathy. 8vo, 2 00
Gesenius's Hebrew and Chaldee Lexicon to the Old Testament Scriptures.
    (Tregelles.). . . . . .Small 4to, half morocco, 5 00
Letteris's Hebrew Bible. 8vo, 2 25

18